THERMODYNAMICS PROBLEMS

IN

SI UNITS

THERMODYNAMICS PROBLEMS
IN
SI UNITS

H. J. SMITH

M.SC.ENG., C.ENG., F.I.MECH E., M.I.PLANT E.
Deputy Head, Department of Mechanical and Production Engineering
The Polytechnic, Brighton

and

J. W. HARRIS

C.ENG., M.I.MECH E., M.I.NUC.E.
Senior Lecturer, Dept. of Mechanical and Production Engineering
The Polytechnic, Brighton

MACDONALD : LONDON

Published in 1970 by
Macdonald & Co. (Publishers) Ltd
49/50 Poland Street
London W.1

SBN 356 03188 8

Printed and bound by Hazell Watson & Viney Ltd
Aylesbury, Bucks

Contents

Preface

This book may be regarded as the SI Unit successor of *Worked Examples in Engineering Thermodynamics* although all the problems are new. It retains the pattern of the previous book in that the questions are presented at the beginning of each chapter and are separated from the model solutions. This arrangement has been commended by many students because it enables the question to be studied and the solution attempted without unintentional reference to the model solution.

A number of changes have been made in the presentation. The most important is that only the first ten questions in each chapter have model solutions. A further twenty unworked problems with answers cover similar topics.

Although the model solutions indicate all the essential steps not all the 'arithmetic' is fully presented. We hope this will encourage the student to work his own way through the solution.

The book is written for revision work and is aimed mainly at the Thermodynamics of Undergraduate and Higher National Diploma and Certificate Courses. None of the questions has been published before although a few have appeared in examination papers of Brighton College of Technology.

The calculations have been made with a slide rule except where obvious inaccuracies would result. Whilst every effort has been made to avoid errors we shall appreciate any comments from readers.

We acknowledge, with thanks, permission from the Principal of Brighton College of Technology to publish examination questions. We gratefully thank Marjorie Smith for her patience in typing the manuscript.

H.J.S.
J.W.H.

Brighton 1970

Symbols

These generally conform to British Standard 1991, parts 1 and 5.

A	area
a	acceleration, acoustic velocity
C	constant
c	specific heat
d	diameter
E	energy, Young's Modulus
F	force, configuration or angle factor, Helmholtz function
f	specific Helmholtz function
G	Gibbs' function
g	acceleration due to gravity, specific Gibbs' function
H	enthalpy, magnetic field strength
h	specific enthalpy, heat transfer coefficient
k	coefficient of thermal conductivity
L	length
M	molecular mass (weight), magnetisation
m	mass
N	number of revolutions
n	number of moles, polytropic index
p	pressure
Q	heat
q	heat generation rate per unit volume
R	gas constant (particular), thermal resistance
R_0	gas constant (molar or universal)
r	ratio
S	entropy
s	specific entropy
T	temperature
t	time
U	internal energy

u	specific internal energy
V	volume
v	specific volume
v	velocity
W	work
$\overline{W}$	weight
x	dryness fraction
z	vertical distance from datum
Z	compressibility factor
α	angle
β	angle, coefficient of cubical expansion
γ	angle, specific heat ratio
δ	angle
ε	emissivity
η	efficiency
θ	angle
ρ	density, resistivity
μ	viscosity
σ	Stefan-Boltzmann constant
ϕ	non-flow availability
ψ	steady-flow availability
ω	specific humidity, angular velocity

Subscripts

f	saturated liquid
g	dry saturated vapour
fg	evaporation
i	solid
ig	sublimation
sat	saturated
sup	superheated
a	axial direction
b	blade
T	constant temperature
p	constant pressure
v	constant volume
h	constant enthalpy
s	constant entropy
w	tangential (whirl) direction

Dotted symbols indicate rates

Symbols marked with an * indicate state where $Ma = 1$

Abbreviations

atm standard atmosphere
°C   temperature on Celsius scale
g   gramme mass
kg   kilogramme mass
m   metre
N   newton
J   joule
K   kelvin (unit of temperature)
KE   kinetic energy
PE   potential energy
W   watt

Prefixes

c 10^{-2}
m 10^{-3}
μ 10^{-6}
k 10^3
M 10^6
G 10^9

Constants

1 bar $= 10^5$ N/m^2
1 atm $= 1\cdot013\,25$ bar $= 760$ mmHg
R_0 $\quad = 8\cdot3143$ kJ/kg mole K
Other constants will be found in Ref 1 and 4, see Appendix B

Note to the Student

Before attempting the problems in any chapter you should be able to answer the questions at the beginning of that chapter immediately and in very few words. If you cannot do so you need more study. A list of references appears on page 164.

1

The Control Mass

Questions

1. Distinguish between closed and open systems.

2. What is meant by a control mass?

3. Define work and heat.

4. Is it correct to say 'The heat content of the system is 5 kJ'?

5. What is a property?

6. Which of the following are properties and which extensive, which intensive? $H\ Q\ u\ h\ v\ S\ p\ T\ W\ V\ s$.

7. If a cat climbs a tree does it
   (a) increase its potential energy,
   (b) do work against gravity,
   (c) lose internal energy?

8. State the first law of thermodynamics for a control mass moving relative to the observer.

9. A certain system has three possible work modes. How many properties must be known to fix its state?

10. Under what conditions would it be reasonable to treat the water substance as a perfect gas?

11. How are the practical Celsius and the Kelvin temperature scales defined?

12. Define the specific heats of a simple compressible substance.

1

Worked Problems

1.1 A horizontal cylinder fitted with a frictionless, gas-tight piston contains ammonia (NH_3) vapour at a pressure of 11·67 bar with a dryness fraction of 0·9 and occupying a volume of 0·001 m³. A slow expansion takes place to a pressure of 4·295 bar, the piston being fully resisted. A $p - V$ trace obtained during this process shows that $pV^{1·25}$ = constant. An atmospheric pressure of 1·1 bar acts on the back of the piston where the effect of the cross-sectional area of the piston rod may be neglected.

Determine the work and heat transfers for the ammonia system and the work transfer via the piston rod.

1.2 A mass of perfect gas at 8 bar, 330°C is contained in a cylinder. Expansion of the form pV^n = constant takes place until the volume is 5 times the initial volume and the pressure is 1 bar.

Calculate the value of n and the work and heat transfers per unit mass.

$$c_p = 14·5 \text{ kJ/kg K}, \gamma = 1·4.$$

1.3 Define an adiabatic process. Show that for a reversible adiabatic process of a given mass of a perfect gas pV^γ = constant.

A mass of 5 kg of CO_2 is compressed in a reversible adiabatic manner from 20 to 80 bar. The initial temperature is 15°C. Find the final temperature, the work transfer and the change of internal energy.

For CO_2 take $\gamma = 1·27$ and treat as a perfect gas.

1.4 (a) Dry saturated steam at a pressure of 80 bar expands in a cylinder so that pv = constant (that is hyperbolically) until the pressure has fallen to 2 bar. Determine the work and heat transfers during the process per unit mass and the final temperature.

(b) Dry air at 80 bar, 400°C expands in a cylinder so that pv = constant until the pressure has fallen to 2 bar. Determine the work and heat transfers per unit mass and the final temperature.

1.5 A reserve fuel tank on a rocket contains 5000 kg of fuel. The rocket accelerates uniformly from 25 to 31 Mm/h in 16 seconds. What force is exerted on the fuel?

1.6 A closed cylinder contains a free frictionless piston. Initially there is 0·03 m³ of oxygen at 4 bar, 50°C on one side of the piston and 0·06 m³ of CH_4 at 4 bar, $-10°C$, on the other side. The cylinder walls and the piston may be regarded as perfect thermal insulators but the oxygen may be heated electrically. If heating takes place so that the volume of the oxygen doubles, find the final state of both gases, the work done by (a) the oxygen, (b) the CH_4, (c) the piston. What is the heat transfer to the oxygen?

Treat both gases as perfect and take c_p for oxygen and methane as 0·92 and 2·0 kJ/kg K respectively.

1.7 Superheated steam at 20 bar, 300°C occupies a volume of 0·0627 m³ in a cylinder where adiabatic expansion takes place behind a fully resisted piston to 1·5 bar. Find the final condition of the steam and the work and heat transfers.

1.8 A mass of 0·5 kg of air at 1 bar, 600 K is compressed to 4 bar during a reversible adiabatic non-flow operation. Estimate the final temperature and the work and heat transfers assuming that the specific heats for air are given by

$$c_p = 0·9161 + 0·225 \times 10^{-3}T$$
$$c_v = 0·6290 + 0·225 \times 10^{-3}T$$
where T is in kelvins.

1.9 A steel rod length 2 m, diameter 1 mm is stretched by applying a load which increases steadily from zero to 50 N. Find the work done if the change in cross-sectional area is negligible and the temperature is constant. Young's Modulus $E = 210 \text{ GN/m}^2$

1.10 Manganese-ammonium sulphate is a paramagnetic salt that obeys Curie's Law, $M = CH/T$ where M is the magnetisation per unit volume in the direction of the magnetic field H, C is the Curie constant and T the absolute temperature.

In a certain state $H = 10^6$ A/m and the temperature is 10 K. If the applied field is trebled, the temperature remaining constant, find the work done for 1 kg mole of salt.

For this salt $C = 0·02$ K, $\rho = 1·83 \times 10^3$ kg/m³ and the molecular mass is 391 kg/kg mole. $\mu_0 = 1·256 \times 10^{-6}$ kg m/A² s².

Unworked Problems

1.11 A boiler steam drum contains equal volumes of saturated water and steam at 0·7 bar gauge reading. There is no air present and the stop valve is closed. The barometric pressure is 1·0 bar. Determine the heat transfer required, in kJ/kg of drum contents, to raise the pressure gauge reading to 25·0 bar, the stop valve remaining shut.   (503 kJ/kg)

1.12 A mass of 1 kg of steam at a constant pressure of 19 bar is admitted to a cylinder displacing a fully resisted piston. The steam then expands hyperbolically (pv = constant) to 13 bar. Calculate the work transfer during the admission if the steam condition remains constant at 0·98 dryness fraction. Determine also the work and heat transfers during the expansion.   (195, 73·9, 84·9 kJ/kg)

1.13 At the beginning of expansion in the cylinder of a reciprocating steam engine the pressure is 12 bar and the temperature 270°C. At the end of the expansion the total volume of the steam is five times the initial volume and the pressure is 1·3 bar. Find the heat transfer during the expansion per unit mass of steam.   (-434 kJ/kg)

1.14 Steam at 2 bar, 0·9 dry is compressed isentropically to 20 bar in a non-flow quasistatic process. Determine the specific work and heat transfers during the process.   (-362 kJ/kg, 0)

1.15 An insulated tank contains 160 litres of water at 20°C which is heated by an immersion heater. A stirrer in the tank absorbs 200 W. After 90 min stirring and heating the temperature of the water has risen by 35 K. State the work and heat transfers for (a) the system whose boundary is the tank and the free surface of the water, (b) the system comprising the water only. The tank is rigid and the expansion of the water may be neglected.

(W = $-23\,400$ kJ, Q = 0;   W = -1080 kJ, Q = 22 320 kJ)

1.16 A small cylinder is supplied with fluid under pressure which acts on a piston 50 mm diameter. The outer face of the piston is subjected to atmospheric pressure of 1·1 bar together with a resistance of 10^{-2} L^2 N where L mm is the linear displacement of the piston from the inner dead centre. If L changes slowly from 60 to 160 calculate (a) the work against the resistance, (b) the work done by the operating fluid.

What is the relation between the volume swept by the piston and the fluid pressure?   (12·93 J, 34·53 J, $1·1 \times 10^5 + 5·09\,L^2$)

1.17 Write an equation expressing the first law of thermodynamics for a stationary closed system (control mass) undergoing a process, defining all the terms involved.

Can the temperature of a given mass of gas be increased without heating? If so define a suitable system and indicate the energy transfers involved.

A mass of 5 kg of air at 20°C, 1·2 bar is compressed in a reversible non-flow isothermal process to a pressure of 6 bar. Calculate for the air system (a) the work done, (b) the change of internal energy and (c) the heat transfer. Have you made any assumptions?

$$(-675 \text{ kJ}, 0, -675 \text{ kJ})$$

1.18 A mass of perfect gas at 14 bar, 20°C occupies 0·3 m³. The gas expands in a non-flow process following the equation $pv^{1\cdot36} = $ constant until the pressure is 3·5 bar. Determine the heat transfer. Take $R = 0\cdot645$ kJ/kg K, $\gamma = 1\cdot39$. 　　　　　　(28 kJ)

1.19 At the start of compression in a diesel engine the pressure and temperature of the air in the cylinder are 0·99 bar and 54°C. Compression follows the law $pv^{1\cdot28} = $ constant and the compression ratio is 16. Determine the pressure and the temperature at the end of the compression and the heat transfer per unit mass during the compression.

$$(34\cdot42 \text{ bar}, 711 \text{ K}, -119 \text{ kJ/kg})$$

1.20 A horizontal cylinder of 12 cm diameter is fitted with a frictionless piston. One end of the cylinder contains 0·006 m³ of air at atmospheric pressure (1·013 bar) and is connected to a deflated balloon having a non-elastic skin. The other end of the cylinder is supplied with a gas at such a pressure that the piston is caused to move slowly through 30 cm whilst the balloon is inflated to 0·002 m³. If the state of the air in the cylinder varies according to $pv = $ constant calculate the work done by (a) the atmosphere, (b) the balloon, (c) the air, (d) the gas and (e) the piston. 　　(−202·6 J, 0, −160·14 J, 362·74 J, 0)

1.21 An unlagged compressed air storage tank has a volume of 0·2 m³. A compressor pumps air into the tank until the pressure reaches 20 bar. The temperature is then 120°C, the compressor is shut down and all valves on pipes connected to the tank are closed. After 30 min the pressure has fallen to 18 bar. What is the temperature in the tank at this time and how much heat has been transferred?

Eventually the air in the tank cools to the surrounding room temperature of 17°C. By how much does the specific energy of the air in the tank then exceed that in the room? Is the air in the tank capable of delivering work utilising a reversible non-flow adiabatic process and if so how much per unit mass? The room pressure is 1 bar.

(81°C, −99·2 kJ, 0, 112 kJ/kg.)

1.22 Refrigerant 12 (freon 12, CF_2Cl_2) is compressed in a cylinder from 3·086 bar to 7·449 bar. If the process is a non-flow reversible adiabatic, the initial condition being dry saturated, find the final condition and the specific work transfer. (4·77 K superheat, −14·9 kJ/kg)

1.23 Mercury vapour at 0·1 bar, 317°C contained in a cylinder fitted with a piston is compressed to 3 bar, 650°C according to the relation $pv^n =$ constant. Calculate the value of n and the work and heat transfer per unit mass. Assume that the specific volume of the mercury varies directly with the absolute temperature at constant pressure.

(1·154, −90·0 kJ/kg, −67·57 kJ/kg)

1.24 A tank containing 3 kg of ammonia (NH_3) at a temperature of 39°C has a volume of 0·2 m³. The tank is cooled until the temperature falls to 16°C. Find the heat transfer required. (−1345 kJ)

1.25 Air at 17°C is to be compressed from 1·1 to 15·4 bar. Find the ratio of the specific work for an isothermal process to that for an adiabatic process. Both processes are non-flow and quasistatic. Compute the final temperature and the changes of internal energy and enthalpy in each case, for unit mass.

(0·938, 17°C, Isothermal zero, Adiabatic 616 K, 234 kJ, 327·6 kJ)

1.26 A cylinder fitted with a piston contains air at a pressure of 1·1 bar occupying a volume of 0·03 m³. An electric heater in the air space causes the volume to double whilst the piston movement is resisted by a spring and atmospheric pressure of 1·1 bar. The spring force is zero in the initial state and is proportional to the piston displacement. The final air pressure is 3 bar.

How much work is done by (a) the air, (b) the spring, (c) the atmosphere? (9 kJ, −5·7 kJ, −3·3 kJ)

1.27 Develop an expression for the rate of heat transfer from a mass of gas undergoing reversible compression obeying the equation $pv^n =$ constant.

During such a compression of 0·1 kg of oxygen the work done by the gas is −6 kJ. The initial temperature and pressure are 10°C and 1·2 bar and the final temperature is 90°C. Find (a) the heat transfer during the compression, (b) the rate of heat transfer when the gas temperature is 50°C if the volume displacement rate at this instant is 0·8 m³/s. Take γ for oxygen as 1·39.   (−0·67 kJ, 17·94 kJ/s)

1.28 A mass of air which may be taken as a perfect gas is taken through the following cycle of non-flow reversible processes:
    1–2 adiabatic compression from 1 bar, 30°C through a volume ratio of 9.
    2–3 constant volume (isochoric) heat transfer until the temperature reaches 2000 K
    3–4 adiabatic expansion to the initial volume.
    4–1 isochoric heat transfer.
    Determine the net work transfer per kg of air and the mean effective pressure of the cycle described.   (533 kJ/kg, 6·90 bar)

1.29 Carbon dioxide CO_2 at a pressure and a temperature of 20 bar and 25°C is contained in a volume of 2 litres in a cylinder where it is compressed until its temperature is 250°C and it then occupies 0·25 litre. Determine the work and heat transfer during the process: (a) if the gas is treated as perfect having the properties of carbon dioxide at 25°C, (b) using mean specific heats obtained from the tables.
     (−11·38 kJ, −0·68 kJ, −0·82 kJ)

1.30 An aluminium bar having a diameter of 0·01 m and a length of 0·3 m is subjected to a tensile force which increases at a uniform rate from zero to 4 kN. Find the work done if the change in cross-sectional area is negligible. How much work is done by the atmosphere when Poisson's ratio is 0·34 and the atmospheric pressure is 1·0 bar? Take E for aluminium as 70 GN/m². Temperature changes are negligible.
     (−0·437 J, −1·165 μJ)

Solutions

1.1 The expansion is fully resisted and may be assumed to be quasistatic. Work done by the NH_3 system =

$$\int_{V_1}^{V_2} p\,dV = \frac{p_1 V_1 - p_2 V_2}{n - 1} = \underline{0·848 \text{ kJ}}$$

since $p_1 = 11·67 \text{ bar} = 1167 \dfrac{\text{kN}}{\text{m}^2}$; $p_2 = 429·5 \dfrac{\text{kN}}{\text{m}^2}$

$$V_1 = 0\cdot001 \text{ m}^3; \qquad V_2 = \left(\frac{p_1}{p_2}\right)^{\frac{1}{n}} V_1 = 2\cdot225 \times 10^{-3} \text{ m}^3$$

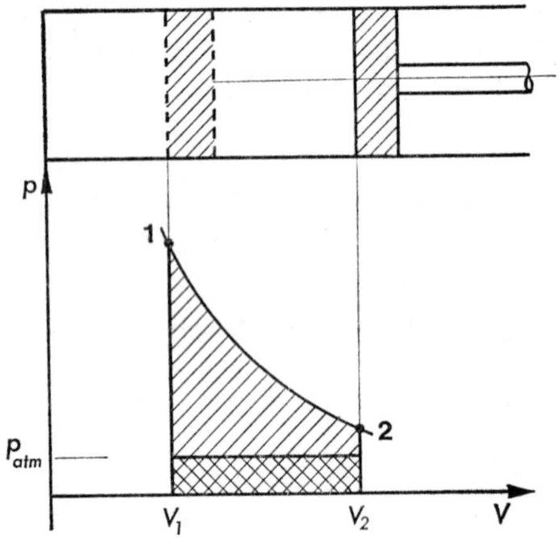

Fig 1.1

The energy equation for the mass of NH_3 concerned is

$$Q - W = \Delta U = U_2 - U_1$$

The tables* do not tabulate internal energy which must be obtained from the specific enthalpy

$$h = u + pv$$

$$\therefore \quad u_1 = h_1 - p_1v_1 = x_1h_g + (1 - x_1)h_f - p_1x_1v_g$$

where the volume of liquid $(1 - x_1)v_f$ is negligible since

$$v_f = \frac{1}{\rho} \approx \frac{1}{600} \frac{\text{m}^3}{\text{kg}}$$

$$\therefore \quad u_1 = [(0\cdot9 \times 1468\cdot9) + (0\cdot1 \times 323\cdot1) - 1167 \times 0\cdot1106 \times 0\cdot9] \frac{\text{kJ}}{\text{kg}}$$

$$= 1238\cdot31 \frac{\text{kJ}}{\text{kg}}$$

$$x_2 = \frac{V_2}{mv_{g2}} \quad \text{where} \quad m = \frac{V_1}{v_1} = \frac{0\cdot001}{0\cdot9 \times 0\cdot1106} = 0\cdot01005 \text{ kg}$$

$$\therefore \quad x_2 = \frac{2\cdot225 \times 10^{-3}}{0\cdot01005 \times 0\cdot2895} = 0\cdot765$$

* Ref 4.

8

$$u_2 = (x_2 h_{g_2} + (1 - x_2)h_{f_2}) - p_2 x_2 v_{g_2} = 1052 \cdot 5 \, \frac{kJ}{kg}$$

$$\therefore \quad Q = (U_2 - U_1) + W = m(u_2 - u_1) + W = \underline{-1 \cdot 017 \, kJ}$$

Work done by piston against atmosphere $= p\Delta V$
$= 110(2 \cdot 225 - 1) \, 10^{-3} = 0 \cdot 135 \, kJ$
Considering the piston as a system in equilibrium, Work delivered $=$ Work received at the gas face $-$ Work against the atmosphere $=$ 0·713 kJ

1.2 Referring to fig 1.1

$$p_1 v_1^n = p_2 v_2^n$$

$$\therefore \quad \frac{p_1}{p_2} = \frac{v_2^n}{v_1^n}$$

$$\therefore \quad \frac{8}{1} = 5^n$$

and

$$\underline{n = 1 \cdot 29}$$

$$W = \int p \, dv = \frac{p_1 v_1 - p_2 v_2}{n - 1}$$

But for unit mass of perfect gas $pv = RT$

$$\therefore \quad W = \frac{p_1 v_1}{n - 1}\left[1 - \left(\frac{p_2}{p_1}\right)^{\frac{n-1}{n}}\right] = \frac{RT_1}{n - 1}\left[1 - \left(\frac{p_2}{p_1}\right)^{\frac{n-1}{n}}\right] \quad (1)$$

Now for a perfect gas $c_p = \dfrac{dh}{dT}$ and $c_v = \dfrac{du}{dT}$

But

$$h = u + pv$$

$$\therefore \quad dh = du + p \, dv + v \, dp$$

and

$$pv = RT$$

$$\therefore \quad p \, dv + v \, dp = R \, dT$$

$$\therefore \quad \frac{dh}{dT} = \frac{du}{dT} + R$$

or

$$c_p = c_v + R$$

$$\therefore \quad R = c_p - c_v = c_p \frac{(\gamma - 1)}{\gamma} = \frac{14 \cdot 5}{3 \cdot 5} = 4 \cdot 14 \, kJ/kg \, K$$

Equation (1) may now be solved giving $\underline{W = 3210 \text{ kJ/kg}}$

Using the energy equation for unit control mass

$$Q = \Delta u + W$$

But $\Delta u = c_v (T_2 - T_1) = \dfrac{R}{\gamma - 1}\left(T_2 - T_1\right)$

$$= \left(\dfrac{n - 1}{\gamma - 1}\right)\left(-W\right)$$

$$\therefore \quad Q = -\left(\dfrac{n - 1}{\gamma - 1}\right)W + W = \left(\dfrac{\gamma - n}{\gamma - 1}\right)W = \underline{883 \text{ kJ/kg}}$$

1.3 An adiabatic process is one during which there is no heat transfer. The control-mass is contained by an adiathermal boundary; that is a boundary impervious to heat.

For a *reversible* process $Tds = dQ$. Hence for a reversible adiabatic process $ds = 0$ and such processes are also *isentropic*.

$$Tds = du + pdv$$

But

$$u = h - pv$$

$$\therefore \quad du = dh - pdv - vdp$$

$$\therefore \quad Tds = dh - vdp$$

For the perfect gas $c_v = \dfrac{du}{dT}; \qquad c_p = \dfrac{dh}{dT} \qquad$ (see 1.2)

and the Tds relations become $ds = c_v\dfrac{dT}{T} + \dfrac{pdv}{T}$

$$ds = c_p\dfrac{dT}{T} - \dfrac{vdp}{T}$$

Thus for the isentropic $\qquad c_v\dfrac{dT}{T} = -\dfrac{Rdv}{v} \qquad$ (i)

$$c_p\dfrac{dT}{T} = \dfrac{Rdp}{p} \qquad \text{(ii)}$$

Dividing (ii) by (i) $\qquad \dfrac{\gamma dv}{v} = \dfrac{dp}{p}$

Integrating $\qquad pv^\gamma = \text{constant}$

$$\frac{p_1 v_1}{T_1} = \frac{p_2 v_2}{T_2} \quad \text{and} \quad p_1 v_1^\gamma = p_2 v_2^\gamma$$

$$\therefore \quad \frac{T_2}{T_1} = \left(\frac{p_2}{p_1}\right)^{\frac{\gamma-1}{\gamma}}$$

$$\therefore \quad T_2 = 288(4)^{\frac{1}{4\cdot7}} = \underline{387 \text{ K}}$$

$$W = \int p\,dV = \frac{p_1 V_1 - p_2 V_2}{\gamma - 1} = \frac{mR(T_1 - T_2)}{\gamma - 1}$$

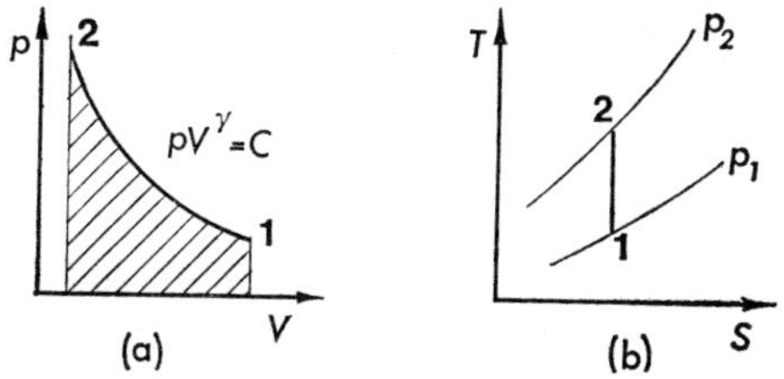

(handwritten margin notes:)
$$P_1 V_1^\gamma = P_2 V_2$$
$$\frac{P_2}{P_1} = \left(\frac{V_1}{V_2}\right)$$
$$\frac{P_1 V_1}{T_1} = \frac{P_2 V_2}{T_2}$$
$$\frac{T_2}{T_1} = \left(\frac{P_2}{P_1}\right)\frac{V_2}{V_1}$$
$$\left(\frac{V_1}{V_2}\right)^\gamma \cdot \left(\frac{V_2}{V_1}\right)$$
$$\frac{T_2}{T_1} = \left(\frac{V_1}{V_2}\right)^{\gamma+1}$$

Fig 1.3

$$R_{CO_2} = \frac{R_0}{44} = \frac{8\cdot3143}{44} \text{ kJ/kg K}$$

$$\therefore \quad W = \underline{-346 \text{ kJ}}$$

The energy equation for the control mass is $Q - W = \Delta U$ and $Q = 0$

$$\therefore \quad \Delta U = -W = \underline{346 \text{ kJ}}$$

1.4 The process is represented by fig 1.1. In both cases the slow expansion in the cylinder may be treated as quasistatic i.e. reversible.

(a) $$W = \int_{v_1}^{v_2} p\,dv = p_1 v_1 \ln \frac{v_2}{v_1} = p_1 v_1 \ln \frac{p_1}{p_2}$$

$$p_1 = 8000 \text{ kN/m}^2; \quad v_1 = v_{g_1} = 0\cdot02352 \text{ m}^3/\text{kg}$$

$$\therefore \quad W = \underline{694 \text{ kJ/kg}}$$

The energy equation is $Q - W = \Delta u$

$$u_1 = u_{g_1} = 2570 \text{ kJ/kg}$$

$$v_2 = \frac{v_1 p_1}{p_2} = 0\cdot02352 \times 40 = 0\cdot9408 \text{ m}^3/\text{kg}$$

$v_{g_2} = 0.8856 \text{ m}^3/\text{kg}$ hence the condition at (2) is superheated
Entering the superheat table at 2 bar and interpolating for u and T in terms of v gives $u_2 = 2565.5 \text{ kJ/kg}$ $\qquad T_2 = \underline{142.4°C}$

$$\therefore \quad Q - 694 \text{ kJ/kg} = (2565.5 - 2570) \text{ kJ/kg}$$

$$Q = \underline{689.5 \text{ kJ/kg}}$$

(b) $\qquad W = p_1 v_1 \ln \dfrac{p_1}{p_2}$ as in case (a) but here $p_1 v_1 = RT_1$

and $W = \underline{713 \text{ kJ/kg}}$

The air may be assumed to be an ideal gas and to obey Boyle's Law. Hence the process is isothermal since $pv = \text{constant}$.

$$T_2 = T_1 = \underline{400°C}$$

The internal energy of an ideal gas depends only on its temperature and is therefore constant along the isotherm. The energy equation then gives

$$Q = W = \underline{713 \text{ kJ/kg}}$$

The difference between these two cases should be considered carefully. It is only for the ideal gas that $pv = \text{constant}$ is the equation of an isotherm.

1.5 The momentum equation for the fuel system is

$$F = \frac{d(mv)}{dt} = ma \text{ where } t \text{ is time}$$

$$a = \frac{6}{3600} \frac{\text{Mm}}{\text{s}} \times \frac{1}{16 \text{s}} \times \frac{10^6 \text{ m}}{\text{Mm}} = 104 \text{ m/s}^2$$

$$F = 104 \frac{\text{m}}{\text{s}^2} \times 5000 \text{ kg} = \underline{520 \text{ kN}}$$

1.6 The methane is thermally insulated and undergoes an adiabatic process for which $pv^\gamma = \text{constant}$ since the gas is perfect.

$$R_{CH_4} = \frac{R_0}{16} = 0.52 \text{ kJ/kg K}$$

$$c_p = \frac{R\gamma}{\gamma - 1}$$

$$\therefore \quad \frac{\gamma - 1}{\gamma} = \frac{0 \cdot 52}{2 \cdot 0} = 0 \cdot 26$$

$$\therefore \quad \gamma = 1 \cdot 35$$

Then using $pv^\gamma = $ constant $\quad p_2 = \underline{10 \cdot 2 \text{ bar}}; \quad T_2 = \underline{335 \text{ K}}$ for CH_4

The final pressure of both gases must be the same since the piston is free.

For O_2 $\qquad\qquad T_2 = \dfrac{p_2 V_2}{p_1 V_1} T_1 = \underline{1647 \text{ K}}$

Work done by the $CH_4 = \dfrac{p_1 V_1 - p_2 V_2}{\gamma - 1} = \underline{-18 \cdot 85 \text{ kJ}}$

This piston is in virtual equilibrium and does zero work, therefore work done on piston by oxygen = work done by piston on methane.

$$\therefore \quad \text{Work done by oxygen} = \underline{18 \cdot 85 \text{ kJ}}$$

$$R_{O_2} = \frac{8 \cdot 3143}{32} = 0 \cdot 26 \text{ kJ/kg K}$$

$$c_v = c_p - R = 0 \cdot 92 - 0 \cdot 26 = 0 \cdot 66 \text{ kJ/kg K}$$

Mass of oxygen =

$$\frac{pV}{RT} = 400 \frac{\text{kN}}{\text{m}^2} \times \frac{0 \cdot 03 \text{ m}^3}{8 \cdot 3143 \text{ kJ}} \times 32 \text{ kg K} \times \frac{1}{323 \text{ K}} = 0 \cdot 143 \text{ kg}$$

Gain of internal energy for oxygen = $mc_v \Delta T$
$$= 0 \cdot 143 \times 0 \cdot 66 \times 1322$$
$$= 125 \text{ kJ}$$

Energy equation for oxygen $Q - W = \Delta U$

$$Q = 125 + 18 \cdot 85 = \underline{143 \cdot 85 \text{ kJ}}$$

1.7 The process may be assumed to be reversible since fluid friction in the cylinder is likely to be negligible. It is therefore isentropic.

$s_2 = s_1 = 6 \cdot 768$ kJ/kg K This is less than s_g at 1·5 bar so condition at (2) must be wet

$$\therefore \quad s_2 = s_{f_2} + x_2 s_{fg_2} \qquad \text{and} \qquad x_2 = \underline{0 \cdot 92}$$

13

The heat transfer is *zero*. This is the meaning of adiabatic. The energy equation becomes $-W = \Delta U = m\Delta u$

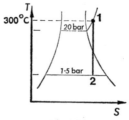

Fig 1.7

$$m = \frac{V}{v} = \frac{0.0627}{0.1255} = 0.5 \text{ kg}$$

$u_1 = 2774 \text{ kJ/kg}$
$u_2 = x_2 u_{g_2} + (1 - x_2)u_{f_2} = 2355 \text{ kJ/kg}$
and $\quad W = \underline{209 \text{ kJ}}$

1.8 Since the gas is not perfect this reversible adiabatic process does not follow $pv^\gamma = $ constant. The differential form of the energy equation is

$$dQ - dW = dU$$

For a reversible process $dW = pdV$

For an ideal gas $\qquad dU = mc_v dT$

Thus the energy equation for the adiabatic becomes

$$0 = mc_v dT + pdV$$

Substituting for $p = \dfrac{mRT}{V}$ and dividing by T

$$O = mc_v \frac{dT}{T} + \frac{mRdV}{V}$$

Let $\quad c_v = b + kT; \qquad c_p = a + kT \quad$ then $\quad R = c_p - c_v = a - b$

and $\qquad O = m\left[\dfrac{bdT}{T} + \dfrac{kTdT}{T} + (a - b)\dfrac{dV}{V} \right]$

Integrating $\quad b \ln T + kT + (a - b)\ln V = $ constant

14

but V is proportional to $\dfrac{T}{p}$

$$\therefore \quad b \ln T + kT + (a - b) \ln \frac{T}{p} = \text{constant}$$

$$a \ln T + kT - (a - b) \ln p = \text{constant}$$

$$a(\ln T_2 - \ln T_1) + k(T_2 - T_1) - (a - b)(\ln p_2 - \ln p_1) = 0$$

$$a \ln T_2 + kT_2 = a \ln T_1 + k T_1 + (a - b)(\ln p_2 - \ln p_1)$$

whence $\quad 0.9161 \ln T_2 + 0.225 \times 10^{-3} T_2 = 6.392$

Solving by trial or plotting gives $T_2 = \underline{875 \text{ K}}$

These linear relations for the specific heats are of limited accuracy. The problem could be solved by using a T–s diagram for air and plotting the isentropic.

1.9 The work done *by the rod* is given by

$$W = -\int_{F_1}^{F_2} F dL$$

$$E = \frac{L}{A}\left[\frac{\partial F}{\partial L}\right]_T$$

This process is at constant temperature

$$dL = \frac{L}{AE} dF$$

$$\therefore \quad W = -\frac{L}{AE}\int_{F_1}^{F_2} F dF = -\frac{L}{2AE} F_2^2 \text{ when } F_1 = 0$$

$$\therefore \quad W = -\frac{2\text{m} \times 50^2 \text{N}^2 \times 4\text{m}^2 \times 10^6}{2 \times 210 \text{ GN} \times \pi \text{ m}^2} = \underline{-0.015 \text{ J}}$$

1.10* $$\qquad\qquad W = -\mu_0 \int_{M_1}^{M_2} V H dM$$

$V = $ volume of 391 kg $= \dfrac{391}{1.83 \times 10^3} = 0.2135 \text{ m}^3/\text{kg mole}$

*This example is included to show that the basic thermodynamics applies to systems other than the simple compressible system. The salt is treated as a simple magnetic system for which the only possible work mode is of the form $dW = HdM$. Hence only two properties are required to express the state, for example T and H, and Curie's Law is analogous to $pV = mRT$ (See Ref 6)

$$M_1 = \frac{CH_1}{T} = 0 \cdot 02 \text{ K} \times 10^6 \text{ A/m} \times \frac{1}{10} \text{ K} = 2 \times 10^3 \text{ A/m}$$

$$M_2 = \frac{C3H_1}{T} = 6 \times 10^3 \text{ A/m}$$

$$W = -\mu_0 \int_{M_1}^{M_2} \frac{VTM}{C} dM = -\frac{\mu_0 VT}{2C}(M_2^2 - M_1^2)$$

$$W = -1 \cdot 256 \times 10^{-6} \frac{\text{kg m}}{\text{A}^2\text{s}^2} \times 0 \cdot 2135 \frac{\text{m}^3}{\text{kg mole}} \times$$

$$\frac{10 \text{ K}}{2 \times 0 \cdot 02 \text{ K}}[6^2 - 3^2]10^6 \frac{\text{A}^2}{\text{m}^2} = \underline{-1 \cdot 81 \text{ kJ/kg mole}}$$

2

The Control Volume

Questions

1. What is a control volume and a control surface?

2. Must a control volume always be fixed in space?

3. If the control volume is in steady state can the mass within the volume change with time?

4. Define enthalpy.

5. What is meant by flow energy or flow work?

6. Write down the steady-flow energy equation and explain the meaning and significance of each term.

7. In what ways can the energy of the control volume be influenced other than by the fluid flows in or out?

8. Is kinetic energy dependent on the gravitational field in which the control volume is situated?

9. Write down a momentum equation for a control volume in steady state with single entry and exit streams.

10. If the control volume is in steady state what can be said about the mass within the control volume?

Worked Problems

2.1 Steam enters a combined power and process plant at a pressure of 40 bar and a temperature of 400°C with a velocity of 80 m/s and leaves as liquid at 2 bar, 90°C with a velocity of 10 m/s. The exit point is 30 m lower than the entry point and the flow rate is 5000 kg/h. If the heat transfer *from* the plant is 150 kW find the work transfer rate.

$$(g = 9.81 \text{ m/s}^2)$$

2.2 A supply of natural gas is required on a site 800 m above storage level. The gas at $-150°C$, 1·1 bar from storage is pumped steadily to a point on the site where its pressure is 1·2 bar, its temperature 15°C and the flow rate 1000 m³/h. If the work transfer to the gas at the pump is 15 kW find the heat transfer to the gas between the two points.

Neglect the change of kinetic energy and assume that the gas has the properties of methane CH_4 which may be treated as a perfect gas having $\gamma = 1.33$. $(g = 9.75 \text{ m/s}^2)$

2.3 Mercury enters a boiler plant at a pressure of 0·6 bar and a temperature of 250·3°C. Mercury vapour leaves at 29 bar, 650°C and is throttled to 20 bar. Find the heat transfer in the boiler per kg of mercury and the condition after throttling. State any assumptions made.

2.4 Air at 1·05 bar, 20°C flows steadily at a rate of 2 m³/min into a compressor where it is raised to a pressure of 15 bar and leaves at a temperature of 120°C. The heat transfer *from* the compressor is 10 per cent of the work transfer *to* the machine. Find these work and heat transfers assuming the air to behave as a perfect gas.

2.5 A perfect gas flows through a nozzle where it expands in a reversible adiabatic manner. The inlet conditions are 22 bar, 500°C, 38 m/s. At exit the pressure is 2 bar. Determine the exit velocity and the exit area if the flow rate is 4 kg/s. Take $R = 0.19$ kJ/kg K, $\gamma = 1.35$

2.6 Steam at 80 bar, 380°C expands during a reversible adiabatic steady-flow process in a turbine to a pressure of 10 bar. Determine from the $h - s$ chart the work transfer for unit mass flow and the condition of the steam leaving the turbine.

2.7 Refrigerant 12 (Freon 12, CF_2Cl_2) enters the condenser of a refrigeration plant at 8·477 bar, 65°C and leaves at 30°C, the loss of pressure being negligible. Cooling water enters at 15°C and leaves at 20°C. Find the mass flow rate of cooling water necessary for unit mass flow rate of refrigerant.

2.8 The stagnation temperature and pressure at entry to a gas turbine are 700°C and 4 bar. After the nozzles the static pressure is 1·5 bar, the nozzle efficiency (total to static) being 93 per cent. After the rotor the static pressure is 1·5 bar, the stagnation pressure 2 bar and the stagnation isentropic efficiency of the turbine is 81 per cent.

Determine (a) the gas stagnation and static temperatures and the velocity at nozzle exit,

(b) the work transfer per unit mass,

(c) the stagnation and static temperatures at the rotor exit.

Treat the gas as perfect with $c_p = 1·0 \text{ kJ/kg K}$, $\gamma = 1·4$

2.9 Two streams of steam are mixed in an adiabatic steady flow process. Stream A is at 5 bar, 300°C and stream B at 5 bar with a dryness fraction of 0·98. The mixed stream at 5 bar is condensed in a tubular feed heater which it leaves at 4·5 bar, 139°C. Water under pressure enters the tubes at 50°C and leaves at 120°C. The heater is well lagged. If the mass flow rate of B is 0·7 of A find the state of the mixed stream and the masses of A and B required per unit mass of feed water.

Kinetic and potential energy changes are negligible.

2.10 A pipe line carrying steam at a steady state of 15 bar and 200°C is connected via a valve to an evacuated rigid vessel having a volume of 0·1 m³. The valve is cracked (that is opened very slightly) so that steam leaks into the vessel until its pressure rises to 10 bar. What is the condition of steam in the vessel at that time and what mass has entered? Neglect heat transfer from the vessel.

2.11 A nozzle of circular section for laboratory use is supplied with 6 kg/min of steam at 20 bar, 300°C through a length of flexible pipe having a bore 3 cm in diameter. The nozzle is designed to expand the steam isentropically to an atmospheric pressure of 1·0 bar. The nozzle is held by a single support at right angles to the nozzle axis.

Determine the force on the support excluding the nozzle weight. The flexible connection may be assumed to exert negligible force on the nozzle.

Unworked Problems

2.12 Write down the steady flow energy equation clearly defining each term.

Steam at 8 bar, 0·97 dry is throttled to 3 bar before entering a

turbine in which it expands to 0·1 bar and is then 0·85 dry. Calculate the power developed by the turbine for a flow of 1 kg/s if there is a heat transfer to the surroundings of 70 kJ/kg. State any assumptions made.
(412·4 kW)

2.13 Steam is generated at 62 bar, 400°C and flows steadily through a control valve which reduces its pressure to 48 bar. The steam then flows through a turbine where it expands adiabatically to 0·07 bar with a dryness fraction of 0·9. Find the steam flow rate (kg/min) required to generate 60 MW. State any assumptions made.
(4275 kg/min)

2.14 Air at a pressure of 1·1 bar flows at a steady rate of 60 kg/min into a system in which there is a negative work transfer rate of 30 kW. The air enters at 27°C with a velocity of 20 m/s and leaves at 50°C, 6·6 bar with a velocity of 100 m/s. The exit point is 50 m above the entry level.

Assuming the air to be a perfect gas for which $c_p = 1·005$ kJ/kg K, determine the heat transfer to the system and the exit area required.
$(g = 9·81$ m/s^2.)

Would removing the system to the moon affect your answer and if so, why?
$(-1·594$ kW, 0·001405 m^2)

2.15 A perfect gas flows steadily through the following systems:
- (*i*) a compressor which it enters at 1·35 bar, 38°C and leaves at 5·4 bar, 278°C. The heat transfer to the gas during this operation is -23 kJ/kg;
- (*ii*) a combustion chamber where it is heated at constant pressure to 390 °C.
- (*iii*) an adiabatic turbine where it expands reversibly to 1·35 bar.

Determine the work transfer rate in systems (*i*) and (*iii*) for a flow rate of 2·5 kg/s and the temperature of the gas leaving the turbine. Neglect changes of potential and kinetic energy and take
$$\gamma = 1·4 \qquad c_p = 1·0 \text{ kJ/kg K}$$
$(-657·5$ kW, 542·5 kW, 446 K)

2.16 A boiler generates 1500 kg/h of steam at 20 bar, 250°C from feed water at 49°C. This steam expands in a turbine to 2·8 bar, 0·95 dryness fraction, at which pressure it condenses and cools to liquid at 102·3°C in a process heater. The boiler fuel has a gross calorific value of 43 700 kJ/kg and the boiler efficiency is 78 per cent. Calculate (a) the fuel consumption rate (b) the turbine power output and (c) the heat transfer rate in the process plant.

(118·8 kg/h, 121·12 kW, 910 kW)

2.17 A turbo-compressor delivers 140 m³/min of air at 2·76 bar, 43°C which is heated at this pressure to 430°C and finally expanded in a turbine which delivers 1860 kW. During the expansion there is a heat transfer of 5·2 MJ/min to the surroundings. Calculate the turbine exhaust temperature if changes of kinetic and potential energy are negligible. (157°C)

2.18 Define the specific heats at constant pressure and constant volume and hence produce expressions for the changes of internal energy and enthalpy of a perfect gas during a process which causes a temperature change ΔT.

A perfect gas has a molecular mass of 28 kg/kg mole and a specific heat ratio, $\gamma = 1·4$. It enters a compressor at $-10°C$ with a pressure of 2 bar and a velocity of 60 m/s. The compressor delivers at 12 bar with a velocity of 5 m/s. The compression is a reversible adiabatic process.

Determine (a) the delivery temperature;
            (b) the work per unit mass

(165°C, 180·2 kJ/kg)

2.19 Sketch typical phase diagrams on p–T and p–v axes for a pure substance that contracts on freezing. Include as much information as possible.

Ammonia NH_3 at $-24°C$, 1·74 bar is heated at constant pressure to 3°C.

Calculate the changes of specific enthalpy, specific volume and specific internal energy.

If 2·5 kg/min of ammonia flow through the heater what is the heating rate?

(1402·65 kJ/kg, 0·799 m³/kg, 1263·65 kJ/kg, 58·5 kW)

2.20 Differentiate between pv and pdv and give examples of the inclusion of these terms in energy equations.

Steam at 7·0 bar, 260°C flows steadily through a nozzle and leaves at 1·1 bar with a dryness fraction of 0·98. If the approach velocity is 152 m/s and the expansion is adiabatic find the exit area required for a flow of 3·6 kg/s. What is the isentropic efficiency of the nozzle?

(65·0 cm², 0·93)

2.21 Waste steam from a process is at a pressure of 1·3 bar and a dryness fraction of 0·73. It is compressed adiabatically in a rotary machine to 4·0 bar, the isentropic efficiency of compression being 76·3 per cent. Calculate the delivery condition and the power required to deal with 1000 kg/h. Use the h–s chart to check your calculation.

Compare the economy of this process with just condensing the waste steam at 1·3 bar and then feeding the condensate to an oil fired boiler having an efficiency of 80 per cent, where steam is generated at the same condition as was produced by the compressor. Assume that the compressor was driven by a Diesel engine of efficiency 38 per cent.

(0·785, 54·6 kW, engine 22·6 per cent of boiler oil consumption)

2.22 A reciprocating air compressor takes in 2 m³/min at 1·1 bar, 20°C which it delivers at 15 bar, 111°C to an after cooler where the air is cooled at constant pressure to 25°C. The power absorbed by the compressor is 4·15 kW. Determine the heat transfer in (a) the compressor and (b) the cooler. State your assumptions. (−0·17 kW, −3·76 kW)

2.23 Air enters a compressor with a velocity of 176 m/s, a static pressure of 1·05 bar and a stagnation temperature of 23·6°C. It is compressed to a stagnation pressure of 7·3 bar with a stagnation isentropic efficiency of 79·5 per cent. The delivery velocity is 92 m/s.

Determine the power and the discharge pipe area required for a volume flow rate of 1032 m³/min measured at intake static conditions. Treat the air as a perfect gas. (5450 kW, 0·0523 m²)

2.24 A turbo-compressor deals with 931·4 kg/min of CO_2. The static pressure and temperature in the intake pipe are 56 bar, 23°C. The intake pipe has a diameter of 5 cm. Delivery stagnation conditions are 100 bar and 77°C. Determine the stagnation isentropic efficiency treating the CO_2 as a perfect gas having $c_p = 0·89$ kJ/kg K.

(68·3 per cent)

2.25 A feed water heater is supplied with steam at 1·3 bar, 0·98 dryness fraction which comes into direct contact with the feed water, the mixture leaving as liquid at 107·1°C. The feed water enters the heater at 38°C. Determine the mass of steam required per kg of feed water.

The feed leaving the heater passes through a feed pump which raises its pressure from 1·3 to 100 bar. The pump operation may be taken as reversible and adiabatic. Find the pump work for unit mass flow and the temperature of the water entering the boiler.

(Note – use the Compressed Water Table) (0·1322 kg, 10·3 kJ/kg, 108°C)

2.26 Superheated steam at a pressure of 130 bar and a temperature of 700°C is to be de-superheated in a steady flow device by a spray of water at 140 bar, 30°C. The discharge from the de-superheater is at 130 bar, 400°C. Find the mass ratio of water to highly superheated steam assuming that kinetic energy changes are negligible. (0·284)

2.27 Compressed air at a static temperature and pressure of 16°C and 5 bar flows through a pipe having a uniform bore of 6 cm which bends through 60°. The velocity of the air entering the bend is 50 m/s and there is a drop in static pressure of 0·1 bar across the bend, the change in static temperature being negligible. What force does the fluid exert on the bend? (1440 N, 59·1°)

2.28 Air enters a gas turbine plant at a rate of 20 kg/s with a velocity of 100 m/s through an inlet area of 0·25 m². The inlet pressure is 0·95 bar and the atmospheric pressure is 1·1 bar. The exhaust is in line with the intake and conditions at the exhaust section, which has an area of 0·1 m², are: velocity 400 m/s, pressure 1·3 bar, mass flow rate 20·25 kg/s. The momentum of the fuel entering the plant is negligible. Determine the thrust on the plant. (4·35 kN)

2.29 A well lagged evacuated vessel of capacity 0·09 m³ is connected to a steam main carrying steam at 10 bar, 0·95 dry. Steam leaks into the vessel which is isolated when the pressure inside has risen to 7 bar. Determine the mass of steam transferred and its final state.

(0·284 kg, 224·4°C)

2.30 A perfectly insulated evacuated vessel, capacity 1 litre, is charged with air from a surrounding atmosphere at 1·1 bar, 21°C. Determine the mass of air that must enter to raise the pressure inside the vessel to 1 bar and the final temperature of the air in the vessel. (0·845 g, 139°C)

Solutions

2.1 Making the assumption that the plant is in steady state the flow energy equation for the passage of unit mass through the control volume is

$$Q - W = (h_2 - h_1) + \frac{v_2^2 - v_1^2}{2} + g(z_2 - z_1)$$

At 40 bar, 400°C the steam is superheated and its enthalpy h_1 may be read from the tables.[*] Thus $h_1 = 3214$ kJ/kg

$$z_1 = 30 \text{ m} \qquad z_2 = 0$$
$$v_1 = 80 \text{ m/s} \qquad v_2 = 10 \text{ m/s}$$

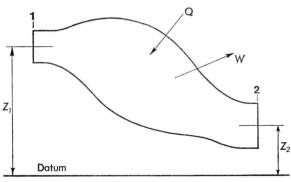

Fig 2.1

The specific enthalpy h_2 of the leaving fluid may be read as h_f at 90°C. Note that this liquid is not boiling since the saturation pressure at 90°C is only 0·7011 bar whereas the actual pressure is 2 bar. Under these conditions the enthalpy of the compressed liquid may be read as h_f at the correct temperature. Corrections for higher differences of pressure are given on page 11 of the Mayhew & Rogers tables.

Hence $\qquad\qquad h_2 = 376·9$ kJ/kg

Substituting in the energy equation

$$Q - W = (376·9 - 3214)\frac{\text{kJ}}{\text{kg}} + \frac{(10^2 - 80^2)}{2}\left[\frac{\text{m}^2}{\text{s}^2}\right]\left[\frac{\text{N s}^2}{\text{kg m}}\right]\left[\frac{\text{kJ}}{10^3\text{N m}}\right]$$

$$+ (0 - 30)\text{m} \times 9·81\left[\frac{\text{m}}{\text{s}^2}\right]\left[\frac{\text{N s}^2}{\text{kg m}}\right]\left[\frac{\text{kJ}}{10^3\text{N m}}\right]$$

$$= -2840·5443 \text{ kJ/kg}$$

This accuracy is not justified and rounding off gives

$$Q - W = -2840·5 \text{ kJ/kg}$$

Note that the changes of kinetic and potential energy are small in

[*] Ref 4.

this problem. Care should always be taken to check their magnitude and not to *assume* that they are negligible.

$$\therefore \quad Q - W = -2840 \cdot 5 \frac{kJ}{kg} \times \frac{5000 \text{ kg}}{3600 \text{ s}} = -3950 \text{ kW}$$

Now
$$Q = -150 \text{ kW}$$

$$\therefore \quad -W = -3950 + 150$$

$$\therefore \quad W = \underline{3800 \text{ kW}}$$

2.2 Since the change of kinetic energy is negligible the steady flow energy equation reduces to

$$Q - W = (h_2 - h_1) + g(z_2 - z_1) \text{ for unit mass flow rate}$$

The gas is perfect, hence $h_2 - h_1 = c_p(T_2 - T_1)$

Now for CH_4 $\quad R = \dfrac{R_0}{M} = \dfrac{8 \cdot 3143}{16} = 0 \cdot 52 \text{ kJ/kg K}$

and
$$c_p = \left[\frac{\gamma}{\gamma - 1} \right] R = \left[\frac{1 \cdot 33}{0 \cdot 33} \right] 0 \cdot 52 = 2 \cdot 1 \text{ kJ/kg K}$$

$$\therefore \quad h_2 - h_1 = 346 \text{ kJ/kg}$$

$$g(z_2 - z_1) = 9 \cdot 75 \frac{m}{s^2} (800 - 0) \text{ m} \frac{kJ}{10^3} \frac{s^2}{m^2 kg} = 7 \cdot 8 \text{ kJ/kg}$$

$$\therefore \quad Q - W = 346 + 7 \cdot 8 = 353 \cdot 8 \text{ kJ/kg}$$

but the flow rate is 1000 m³/h at the second point.

$$\therefore \quad \dot{m} = \frac{p\dot{V}}{RT} = 120 \frac{kN}{m^2} \times 1000 \frac{m^3}{h} \times \frac{1}{0 \cdot 52} \frac{kg K}{kJ} \times \frac{1}{288 \text{ K}} = 802 \text{ kg/h}$$

$$\therefore \quad Q - W = 802 \frac{kg}{h} \times 353 \cdot 8 \frac{kJ}{kg} \times \frac{1}{3600} \frac{h}{s} = 78 \cdot 9 \text{ kW}$$

$$\therefore \quad Q = 78 \cdot 9 - 15 = \underline{63 \cdot 9 \text{ kW}}$$

2.3 Assuming steady flow, negligible feed pump work and negligible changes of KE and PE

$$Q = h_2 - h_1$$

Now $h_1 = h_f$ at 250·3°C approximately $= 34·33$ kJ/kg
$h_2 = h_g$ at 29 bar $+ c_p(T - T_{\text{sat}})$

Using linear interpolation for h_g

$$h_2 = 370 \cdot 93 + 0 \cdot 1036(650 - 626) = 373 \cdot 415 \text{ kJ/kg}$$

$$\therefore \quad Q = 339 \cdot 09 \text{ kJ/kg}$$

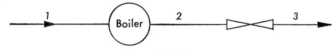

Fig 2.3

For a throttle valve with negligible heat transfer and negligible changes of KE and PE the steady flow energy equation becomes

$$0 = h_3 - h_2$$

$$\therefore \quad h_3 = h_2 = 373 \cdot 415 \text{ kJ/kg}$$

But $$h_g \text{ at 20 bar} = 366 \cdot 47 \text{ kJ/kg}$$

$$\therefore \quad \text{Superheat} = 6 \cdot 945 \text{ kJ/kg}$$

$$\therefore \quad \underline{\text{Degree of superheat}} = \frac{6 \cdot 945}{0 \cdot 1036} = \underline{67 \text{ K}}$$

2.4 In the absence of other information we must assume that the changes of KE and PE are negligible. The steady flow energy equation then reduces to

$$Q - W = \dot{m}(h_2 - h_1)$$

Since the gas is perfect $\dot{m}(h_2 - h_1) = \dot{m}c_p(T_2 - T_1)$

Now $$\dot{m} = \frac{p\dot{V}}{RT} = 105 \frac{\text{kN}}{\text{m}^2} \times 2 \frac{\text{m}^3}{\text{min}} \times \frac{1}{0 \cdot 2871} \frac{\text{kg K}}{\text{kJ}} \times \frac{1}{293 \text{ K}} \times \frac{\text{kJ}}{\text{m kN}}$$

$$= 2 \cdot 5 \text{ kg/min}$$

$$\therefore \quad Q - W = 2 \cdot 5 \frac{\text{kg}}{\text{min}} \times 1 \cdot 005 \frac{\text{kJ}}{\text{kg K}} \times 100 \text{ K} \times \frac{1}{60} \frac{\text{min}}{\text{s}} = 4 \cdot 18 \text{ kW}$$

Remember that Q is the heat transfer *to* the control volume and W is the work transfer *from* the control volume

$$0 \cdot 1W - W = 4 \cdot 18 \text{ kW}$$

$$\therefore \quad W = -\frac{4 \cdot 18}{0 \cdot 9} = \underline{-4 \cdot 65 \text{ kW}}$$

$$\therefore \quad Q = \underline{-0 \cdot 465 \text{ kW}}$$

Note that the work transfer *to* the compressor is 4·65 kW and therefore the heat transfer *from* the compressor is 0·465 kW

2.5 The steady flow energy equation with $Q = 0$ (adiabatic), $W = 0$, and the change of potential energy negligible is

$$0 = (h_2 - h_1) + \left[\frac{v_2^2 - v_1^2}{2}\right]$$

and for a perfect gas $(h_2 - h_1) = c_p(T_2 - T_1)$

$$\therefore \quad \left[\frac{v_2^2 - v_1^2}{2}\right] = c_p(T_1 - T_2)$$

$$c_p = \left[\frac{\gamma}{\gamma - 1}\right]R = 0\cdot734 \text{ kJ/kg K}$$

$$\therefore \quad \left[\frac{v_2^2 - 38^2}{2}\right]\frac{\text{m}^2}{\text{s}^2} = 0\cdot734 \frac{\text{m kN}}{\text{kg K}} \times (T_1 - T_2)\text{ K} \times \frac{10^3 \text{ kg m}}{\text{kN s}^2} \quad (1)$$

Now since the gas is perfect we have, for a reversible adiabatic,

$$T_2 = T_1\left[\frac{p_2}{p_1}\right]^{\left(\frac{\gamma - 1}{\gamma}\right)} = 773\left[\frac{2}{22}\right]^{\left(\frac{0\cdot35}{1\cdot35}\right)} = 416 \text{ K}$$

Then solving equation (1) $v_2 = \underline{723 \text{ m/s}}$

By using the continuity equation we have

$$A_2 = \frac{\dot{m}}{\rho_2 v_2} = \frac{\dot{m}RT_2}{p_2 v_2} = 4\frac{\text{kg}}{\text{s}} \times 0\cdot19 \frac{\text{kN}}{\text{kg K}} \times \frac{416 \text{ K m}^2}{200 \text{ kN}} \times \frac{1}{723}\frac{\text{s}}{\text{m}}$$

$$= \underline{0\cdot002185 \text{ m}^2}$$

2.6   Since $\displaystyle\int\left(\frac{dQ}{T}\right)_{Rev} = \Delta s$ and $dQ = 0$

$$\therefore \quad \Delta s = 0$$

Plotting the isentropic process on the *h–s* chart as indicated in fig 2.6

$$h_1 - h_2 = 445 \text{ kJ/kg}$$

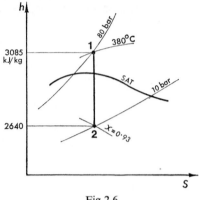

Fig 2.6

The steady flow energy equation assuming negligible changes of both potential and kinetic energy is

$$-W = h_2 - h_1$$

$$\therefore \quad -W = -445 \text{ kJ/kg or } W = \underline{445 \text{ kJ/kg}}$$

The exit condition is a dryness fraction of $\underline{0\cdot93}$

2.7

Consider the control volume B

$$Q = h_2 - h_1 \text{ since } W = 0 \text{ and } \Delta\text{PE and } \Delta\text{KE are negligible}$$

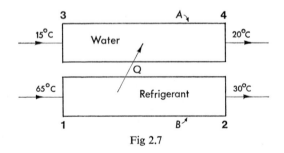

Fig 2.7

From the tables

$$h_1 = 223\cdot73 \text{ kJ/kg for 30K superheat}$$

$$h_2 = 64\cdot59 \text{ kJ/kg (pressure effect negligible)}$$

$$\therefore \quad Q = -159\cdot14 \text{ kJ/kg R12}$$

∴ for the control volume A $Q = 159\cdot14$ kJ/kg R12 and the energy equation is $Q = m(h_4 - h_3)$

where m is the flow of water/kg R12

$$\therefore \quad 159\cdot14 \text{ kJ/kg R12} = mc(T_4 - T_3) = m \times 4\cdot18 \frac{\text{kJ}}{\text{kg K}} \times 5 \text{ K}$$

$$\therefore \quad m = \frac{159\cdot14}{4\cdot18 \times 5} \text{ kg/kg R12} = \underline{7\cdot6 \text{ kg/kg R12}}$$

2.8 Consider the control surface formed by the nozzle wall and its entry and exit planes. The energy equation for this control volume is

$$0 = (h_2 - h_1) + \frac{v_2^2 - v_1^2}{2} \tag{1}$$

since $Q = 0$ (adiabatic) $W = 0$ (no moving boundary, shafts crossing the boundary or electric currents) and the change of potential energy is negligible.

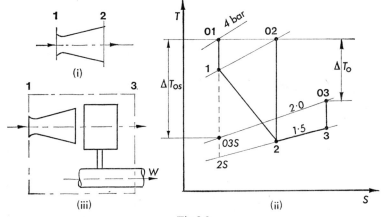

Fig 2.8

The stagnation enthalpy is defined as

$$h_0 = h + \frac{v^2}{2}$$

So that for the nozzle $h_{01} = h_{02}$ and $c_p T_{01} = c_p T_{02}$

$$\therefore \quad T_{01} = T_{02}$$

$$\therefore \quad T_{02} = \underline{973 \text{ K}}$$

29

$$\text{Nozzle efficiency} = \frac{T_{01} - T_2}{T_{01} - T_{2s}} = 0.93$$

For the isentropic process $1_0 - 2_s$

$$T_{2s} = T_{01}\left[\frac{p_2}{p_{01}}\right]^{\frac{\gamma-1}{\gamma}} = 973\left[\frac{1.5}{4}\right]^{\frac{1}{3.5}} = 736 \text{ K}$$

$$\therefore \quad \frac{973 - T_2}{973 - 736} = 0.93 \qquad \therefore \quad T_2 = \underline{752 \text{ K}}$$

Since c_p is constant equation (1) becomes

$$\frac{v_2^2 - v_1^2}{2} = c_p(T_1 - T_2)$$

But $\qquad T_1 = T_{01} - \frac{v_1^2}{2c_p} \qquad \therefore \quad \frac{v_2^2}{2} = c_p(T_{01} - T_2)$

$$\therefore \quad \tfrac{1}{2}v_2^2 = 1.0\,\frac{\text{kJ}}{\text{kg K}} \times 221 \text{ K} \times 10^3\,\frac{\text{kg m}^2}{\text{kJ s}^2}$$

$$\therefore \quad v_2 = \underline{663 \text{ m/s}}$$

$$\text{Stagnation isentropic efficiency} = \frac{T_{01} - T_{03}}{T_{01} - T_{03s}}$$

$$T_{03s} = T_{01}\left[\frac{p_{03}}{p_{01}}\right]^{\frac{\gamma-1}{\gamma}} = 973\left[\frac{2.0}{4.0}\right]^{\frac{1}{3.5}} = 800 \text{ K}$$

$$\therefore \quad \frac{973 - T_{03}}{973 - 800} = 0.81 \qquad T_{03} = \underline{833 \text{ K}}$$

$$\therefore \quad T_{01} - T_{03} = 140 \text{ K}$$

Consider the control volume shown in fig 2·8 (iii).

Since $Q = 0 \qquad -W = (h_3 - h_1) + \frac{v_3^2 - v_1^2}{2}$

$$= (h_{03} - h_{01}) = c_p(T_{03} - T_{01})$$

$$\therefore \quad W = c_p(T_{01} - T_{03})$$

$$= 1.0\,\frac{\text{kJ}}{\text{kg K}} \times 140 \text{ K} = \underline{140 \text{ kJ/kg}}$$

$$\frac{T_{03}}{T_3} = \left[\frac{p_{03}}{p_3}\right]^{\frac{\gamma-1}{\gamma}} = \left[\frac{2}{1\cdot5}\right]^{\frac{1}{3\cdot5}} = 1\cdot0856$$

$$\therefore \quad T_3 = \frac{833}{1\cdot0856} = \underline{767 \text{ K}}$$

2.9

Control Volume I

$Q = 0$ (adiabatic) $W = 0$ (no moving parts or electric currents)

$$\Delta KE \text{ and } \Delta PE = 0$$

$$\therefore \quad 0 = H_{\text{out}} - H_{\text{in}}$$

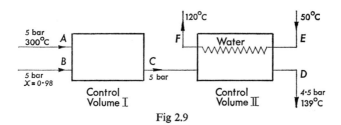

Fig 2.9

Note that because more than one stream is involved we must take the masses of the streams into account.

$$H_{\text{out}} = (m_A + m_B)h_C = 1\cdot7m_Ah_C$$

$$H_{\text{in}} = m_Ah_A + m_Bh_B = m_A(h_A + 0\cdot7h_B)$$

$$= m_A(3065 + 0\cdot7[640 + 0\cdot98 \times 2109]) = 4959\cdot8m_A$$

$$\therefore \quad h_C = \frac{4959\cdot8\ m_A}{1\cdot7\ m_A} = 2918 \text{ kJ/kg}$$

Using the superheat table the state at C is superheated steam at 5 bar, 228°C

Control Volume II

$$Q = 0 \qquad W = 0 \qquad \Delta PE = \Delta KE = 0$$

Again $H_{\text{out}} = H_{\text{in}}$

For the passage of 1 kg of water through the control volume

$$H_{out} = h_F + m_C h_D = 505 + m_C 584$$

$$H_{in} = h_E + m_C h_C = 209 \cdot 3 + m_C 2918$$

$$\therefore \quad 505 - 209 \cdot 3 = m_C(2918 - 584)$$

$$\therefore \quad m_C = 0 \cdot 127 \text{ kg/kg water}$$

$$m_A = \underline{0 \cdot 0747 \text{ kg/kg water}}$$

$$m_B = \underline{0 \cdot 0523 \text{ kg/kg water}}$$

2.10

There is inflow to the control volume but no outflow and both the mass and energy content are changing.

$$Q - W = H_{leaving} - H_{entering} + \Delta U \text{ control volume}$$

Now both Q and W are zero and $H_{leaving} = 0$

$$\therefore \quad H_{entering} = m_2 u_2 - m_1 u_1$$

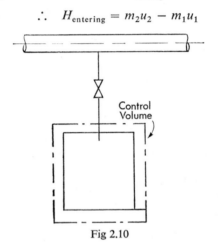

Fig 2.10

Since the vessel was initially evacuated $m_1 = 0$ and $m_2 = $ mass entering

$$\therefore \quad m_2 h_{ent} = m_2 u_2$$

$$\therefore \quad h_{ent} = u_2 = 2796 \text{ kJ/kg}$$

Hence from the table at 10 bar this value of u is found against 300°C approx.

The steam condition is superheated at 10 bar 300°C.

At this condition $v = 0 \cdot 2580 \text{ m}^3/\text{kg}$

$$\therefore \quad m_2 = \frac{0 \cdot 1 \ \text{m}^3}{0 \cdot 2580 \ \text{m}^3/\text{kg}} = \underline{0 \cdot 3875 \ \text{kg}}$$

2.11

$$v_1 = 0 \cdot 1255 \ \text{m}^3/\text{kg} \qquad A_1 = \frac{0 \cdot 03^2 \pi}{4} = 7 \cdot 06 \times 10^{-4} \ \text{m}^2$$

$$v_1 = \frac{\dot{m} v_1}{A_1} = \frac{0 \cdot 1 \times 0 \cdot 1255}{7 \cdot 06 \times 10^{-4}} = 17 \cdot 75 \ \text{m/s}$$

$$h_1 = 3025 \ \text{kJ/kg}$$

$h_2 = 2450 \ \text{kJ/kg}$ from the $h–s$ chart see fig. 2.11 (ii)

$$x_2 = 0 \cdot 9 \qquad \therefore \quad v_2 = 0 \cdot 9 \ v_g = 0 \cdot 9 \times 1 \cdot 694 = 1 \cdot 525 \ \text{m}^3/\text{kg}$$

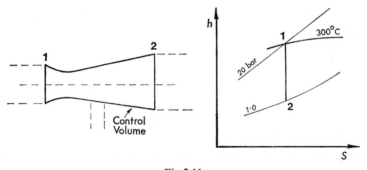

Fig 2.11

Using the energy equation with $Q = W = 0$ and assuming that v_1 is negligible compared with v_2

$$v_2 = (h_1 - h_2)^{\frac{1}{2}} = (2 \times 575 \times 10^3)^{\frac{1}{2}} = 1072 \ \text{m/s}$$

Using the momentum equation we have that the net force on the duct in a direction opposite to that of fluid motion is

$$*F = \dot{m}(v_2 - v_1) + A_2(p_2 - p_a) - A_1(p_1 - p_a)$$

$$= 0 \cdot 1 \frac{\text{kg}}{\text{s}} (1072 - 17 \cdot 75) \frac{\text{m}}{\text{s}} + 0 - 7 \cdot 06 \times 10^{-4} \ \text{m}^2 \times 1900 \frac{\text{kN}}{\text{m}^2}$$

$$\times \frac{10^3 \text{N}}{\text{kN}} = -1235 \ \text{N} \qquad \text{i.e.} \quad \underline{1235 \ \text{N in direction of flow}}$$

* Ref 7 section 18.4

33

3

The Second Law

Questions

1. State the second law for an isolated system in terms of entropy change

2. Is a state having a high entropy more probable than a state having a lower entropy?

3. Distinguish between a macrostate and a microstate.

4. Is it correct to say that a system in equilibrium is always in the same microstate?

5. Can the entropy of a system ever be decreased?

6. An analysis of a process shows an entropy production of -0.02 kJ/kg K What comment can you make on this result?

7. Define thermodynamic temperature and pressure in terms of partia differentials.

8. Why is equilibrium between parts of an isolated system obtained wher the entropy of the system is a maximum?

9. State two *Tds* relations for a simple compressible substance.

10. Does the availability of a system in a given state differ from the internal energy of that system?

11. Under what circumstances does $ds = \dfrac{dQ}{T}$?

12. Are absolute entropy values possible?

Worked Problems

3.1 Dry saturated ammonia vapour at 12·37 bar is cooled at constant pressure until the dryness fraction is 0·8. Adiabatic expansion then takes place to 4·295 bar with an isentropic efficiency of 0·83. Determine the changes of entropy during (a) cooling, (b) expansion; the work and heat transfers per kg and the final state if the whole process is under steady flow conditions. Explain why the loss of entropy during cooling does not contradict the second law of thermodynamics.

3.2 Develop an expression for the change of specific entropy of a perfect gas.

A mass of 2 kg of nitrogen at a pressure of 1·5 bar and a temperature of 20°C is compressed in a non-flow process to 30 bar. The compression follows the relation $pV^{1·28}$ = constant. Find the final temperature, the heat and work transfers and the change of entropy. Assume that the specific heats over the temperature range are constant at their values for the mean temperature.

3.3 For a limited temperature range the specific heats of an ideal gas vary linearly with temperature as follows:

$$c_p = a + kT \qquad c_v = b + kT$$

where $\qquad a = 1·008 \quad$ and $\quad b = 0·819$ kJ/kg K

$\qquad k = 2·18 \times 10^{-4}$ kJ/kg K^2

Derive an expression for the change of specific entropy of this gas in terms of the initial and final pressures and temperatures. A mass of 5 kg of this gas at 1400 K, 6 bar is expanded in a steady flow isentropic process to 1·5 bar. Determine the work and heat transfers and the change of internal energy.

$$R \text{ for the gas} = 0·189 \text{ kJ/kg K}$$

3.4 Steam generated at a pressure of 70 bar and a temperature of 400°C is supplied to a turbine via a throttle valve which reduces the pressure to 60 bar. Expansion in the turbine is adiabatic to a pressure of 2 bar, the isentropic efficiency being 82 per cent. The surroundings are at 20°C, 1·1 bar. Determine the availability of the steam before and after the throttle valve and at the turbine exhaust and calculate the specific work output from the turbine. Kinetic and potential energy changes between the state points concerned are negligible.

3.5 The cylinder of an internal combustion engine contains gases at 2500°C, 58 bar at top dead centre. Expansion takes place through a volume ratio of 9 and the p–v curve has the equation $pv^{1.38}$ = constant. The surroundings are at 20°C, 1·1 bar.

Determine the loss of availability, the work transfer and the heat transfer per unit mass. Treat the gases as perfect having $R = 0.26$ kJ/kg K and $c_v = 0.82$ kJ/kg K

3.6 Air enters a rotary compressor at 1·1 bar, 21°C where it is compressed adiabatically to 6·6 bar, 250°C. Calculate the irreversibility and the entropy production for unit mass flow rate. The temperature of the surroundings is 20°C and the atmospheric pressure is 1·03 bar. Neglect changes of kinetic energy.

3.7 A designer estimates that 0·2 kg of dichlorodifluoromethane (Refrigerant 12) at a pressure of 13·66 bar, temperature 85°C and specific volume 0·0151 m^3/kg will expand in a cylinder following the quasi-static expansion relation $pv^{0.93}$ = constant until the pressure is 6·516 bar. What must be the minimum temperature of the cylinder walls for this to be feasible? (At 6·516 bar, 70°C $v = 0.0344$ m^3/kg and linear interpolation may be used at this pressure)

3.8 The exhaust from a gas turbine at 800 K, 1·12 bar flows steadily into a heat exchanger which cools the gas to 700 K without significant pressure drop. The heat transfer from the gas heats an air flow at constant pressure which enters the exchanger at 470 K. The mass flow rate of air is twice that of the gas and the surroundings are at 1·03 bar, 20°C.

Determine (a) the decrease in availability of the exhaust gases and (b) the entropy production per kg of products.

What arrangement would be necessary to make the heat transfer theoretically reversible and by how much would this increase the power output of the plant per kg of turbine gas?

Take $c_p = 1.08$ kJ/kg K for the exhaust gas and 1·05 kJ/kg K for the air.

Neglect heat transfers to the surroundings and changes of kinetic and potential energy.

3.9 Define the enthalpy h, Gibbs function g and the Helmholtz function f for a simple compressible substance. Use these definitions in conjunction with the state equation $Tds = du + pdv$ to derive the Maxwell relations.

Show that isobars are straight lines in a two-phase region on the
h–s diagram for such a substance.

3.10 The gas neon (Ne) has a molecular mass of 20·183 and its critical
temperature, pressure and volume are 44·5 K, 27·3 bar and 0·0416
m³/kg mole. Reading from a compressibility chart for a reduced
pressure of 2 and a reduced temperature of 1·3, the compressibility
factor Z is 0·7. What are the corresponding specific volume, pressure,
temperature and reduced volume?

Show that the change of enthalpy for the neon along an isotherm is
given by

$$(dh)_T = -\frac{RT^2}{p}\left[\frac{\partial Z}{\partial T}\right]_p dp$$

Unworked Problems

3.11 Superheated steam at 70 bar, 450°C is throttled to 60 bar and then
expands to 2 bar in a steady flow reversible adiabatic process.
Calculate, using the steam tables, the work transfer and the final state
of the steam. State any assumptions that you make. Check your
calculations by using the h–s chart for steam. .

(752 kJ/kg; 0·922)

3.12 Mercury vapour at 0·1 bar with a dryness fraction of 0·5 is compressed
in an adiabatic steady flow process having an isentropic efficiency of
71 per cent, until the pressure is 10 bar. Calculate the final state and the
work transfer for unit mass.

(0·718; −95·8 kJ/kg)

3.13 A perfect gas having a molecular mass of 40 kg/kg mole and $\gamma = 1\cdot67$
undergoes a state change from 2·5 bar, 20°C to 15 bar, 800°C.
Working from fundamental state equations derive an expression for
change of entropy for the gas system and calculate this change for
a mass of 2 kg. Are you able to make any statement about the
change of entropy of the system surroundings?

(0·6 kJ/kg)

3.14 Deduce a general expression in terms of temperatures and volumes
for the change of entropy of a gas whose specific heats vary linearly
with temperature according to the relations:

$$c_p = a + kT \qquad c_v = b + kT$$

A mass of 0·23 kg of this gas at 1·38 bar, 37·7°C is compressed isentropically through a volume ratio of 9 and then heated at constant volume to 2220 K. Show that the temperature at the end of the isentropic compression is about 767 K and calculate the heat transfer required and the final pressure.

$$a = 13\cdot4, \quad b = 9\cdot25 \text{ kJ/kg K}, \quad k = 17\cdot75 \times 10^{-4} \text{ kJ/kg K}^2$$

(3970 kJ, 88·7 bar)

3.15 An isolated system is such that its state is fixed when its internal energy u and volume v are known. If the system is in two rigid parts separated by a rigid diathermal wall deduce the condition for thermal equilibrium between the parts. Hence define the thermodynamic temperature in terms of property derivatives and show that c_v must be positive.

3.16 The specific heats of an ideal gas vary linearly with temperature such that $c_p = a + kT$, $c_v = b + kT$.

Show that an isentropic process for this gas will have the equation

$$T^b \, v^{(a-b)} \, e^{kT} = \text{constant}$$

If for a given gas $a = 13\cdot39$, $b = 9\cdot24$ kJ/kg K, $k = 1\cdot73 \times 10^{-3}$ kJ/kg K^2 for temperatures between 700 K and 1400 K, determine the volume ratio for an isentropic compression between these two temperatures. If the compression is non-flow, what is the specific work transfer? (6·25; −7·739 MJ/kg)

3.17 Dichlorodifluoromethane (Refrigerant 12) vapour at −15°C with a dryness fraction of 0·2 is heated whilst flowing steadily at a rate of 1 kg/s through a coil of piping submerged in liquid at 80°C until it is at a pressure and temperature of 1·509 bar and −5°C. It is then compressed in a non-adiabatic process for which the reversible work between the same end states is 88 per cent of the actual work, until the pressure is 12·19 bar and the temperature 80°C. Determine the work and heat transfers and the entropy production for each process. Changes of kinetic and potential energy are negligible and the temperature of the surroundings is 20°C.

(0, −46 kW; 133·69 kW, −3·43 kW; 0·1517 and 0·0188 kJ/K s)

3.18 At full load 2265 kg/h of steam is supplied to a turbine at 70 bar, 500°C and exhausts to a condenser at 0·07 bar. A part load may be obtained by throttling the supply to 55 bar.

Determine the specific consumption in kg/kWh and the availability of the steam entering the turbine in each case. Use an isentropic efficiency of 0·8 throughout and take the surrounding pressure and temperature as 1·01 bar, 25°C. The volume flow rate through the nozzles may be assumed to be constant.

How could the loss of availability be avoided?

(4·53, 4·68 kg/kWh; 1386, 1361 kJ/kg)

3.19 A turbo-compressor aspirates gas at 0·3 bar, 58°C and delivers at 1·2 bar. Its polytropic efficiency is 79 per cent and the surroundings are at 15°C, 1·01 bar.

Calculate (a) the isentropic efficiency,
(b) the specific availability of the gas entering and leaving the compressor,
(c) the minimum specific work input required to give the same end states.

$R = 2·08$ kJ/kg K, $\gamma = 1·63$. All the properties given may be taken as stagnation values but the kinetic energy at entry is negligible.

(73·4 per cent, $-711·45$, 793·85, 1505·3 kJ/kg)

3.20 An insulated tank having a volume of 1 m³ contains 0·11 m³ water and 0·89 m³ steam at a pressure of 5 bar. It is connected via a valve to a pipe through which steam is flowing at constant pressure and temperature of 10 bar and 250°C. The valve is opened slightly and after a time the pressure in the tank has risen to 8 bar. Determine the mass of steam that enters, the final condition in the tank and the entropy production. (4·78 kg, 0·0343, 0·8 kJ/K)

3.21 Quote one of the common statements of the Second Law of Thermodynamics.

A steady flow device is proposed taking in saturated liquid ammonia at 16°C and delivering ammonia at 2·077 bar, 82°C. No work transfers are involved but a 'heat reservoir' at 150°C is available. Make caclulations to show whether or not this device is thermodynamically possible, changes of potential and kinetic energy being negligible.

What would be the maximum possible increase in kinetic energy for your answer to remain valid, the initial and final states of the fluid remaining unchanged?

(Entropy production 2·068 kJ/kg K; 876 kJ/kg)

3.22 Steam is supplied to a reversible adiabatic turbine at 100 bar, 600°C. After expansion to 7 bar some steam is bled off and mixed with the condensate coming from the condenser at 39°C. The remaining steam expands through the turbine to 0·07 bar and then condenses. The water leaving the feed heater is pumped into the boiler.
Calculate for 1 kg of boiler steam:

(a) the mass proportion of steam bled if the feed is heated to 150°C;
(b) the turbine work;
(c) the availability of the steam entering the turbine if the surroundings are at 25°C, 1·01 bar;
(d) the irreversibility of the feed heater.
$$(0·174; \quad 1351 \text{ kJ/kg}; \quad 1575 \text{ kJ/kg}; \quad 53·8 \text{ kJ/kg})$$

3.23 Carbon dioxide gas enters a counter-flow heat exchanger at a rate of 136 kg/s at 336°C and leaves at 140°C. Water enters at a rate of 10 kg/s and 66°C and is converted to steam under a constant pressure of 15 bar. Determine the condition of the steam and the irreversibility of the process if the surroundings are at 21°C, 1·01 bar. Neglect all losses. $\qquad$ (281·1°C; 1600 kW)

3.24 At a point (1) early in the expansion stroke of an internal combustion engine the pressure is 55 bar and the temperature 1500 K. The expansion follows the relation $pv^{1·38}$ = constant until the volume is 7·5 times that at (1). The mean temperature of the surroundings is 60°C. Determine the irreversibility of the process for unit mass of cylinder contents for which $R = 0·287$ kJ/kg K, $c_v = 0·87$ kJ/kg K.
$$(62·55 \text{ kJ/kg})$$

3.25 A tank contains 80 kg of compressed nitrogen at 100 bar, 25°C. The surroundings are at 1·00 bar, 25°C. Distinguish between the availability and the energy content of the nitrogen. Calculate the non-flow availability of the nitrogen allowing for the work done against the surroundings.

Determine the maximum possible useful work that could be obtained by reducing the pressure of the nitrogen to 5 bar, the temperature remaining at 25°C. What heat transfer would be necessary?
$$(25\,560 \text{ kJ}; \quad 19\,860 \text{ kJ}; \quad 19\,860\text{kJ})$$

3.26 A control volume has a single entering and a single leaving steady-flow stream and is in steady state. Explain what is meant by the entropy production of this control volume and write an equation giving this quantity. State the Second Law of Thermodynamics in terms of the entropy production.

Steam at 2 bar having a dryness of 0·88 enters an adiabatic diffuser at a velocity of 700 m/s and leaves with low velocity. The isentropic efficiency of compression is 0·79. Estimate the final pressure and the entropy production for a flow rate of 3 kg/s. (6·4 bar; 0·36 kJ/K s)

3.27 A design includes a flow system where superheated Refrigerant 12 at 25·38 bar, 115°C flows steadily through a cooler in which heat transfer occurs to water having a mean temperature of 30°C. The pressure is said to rise during the cooling until the condition of the fluid becomes dry saturated at 100°C. Changes of kinetic and potential energy are negligible and no work is done. Make calculations to show whether this design is feasible.

(Entropy production 0·0094 kJ/kg K)

3.28 Deduce the following property relations for a simple compressible substance.

$$\left[\frac{\partial p}{\partial T}\right]_s = \frac{c_p}{TV\beta}$$

The Gibbs' equation (*Tds* relation) and any Maxwell relation need not be derived.

A substance obeys the Van der Waals state equation.

Explain how this data, together with an experiment, would enable c_p to be calculated from the given property relations.

Find an expression for c_p in terms of $\left[\dfrac{\partial p}{\partial T}\right]_s$ and the constants R. a and b.

3.29 The critical conditions for sulphur dioxide SO_2 are 430·7 K, 79 bar. A single-acting sulphur dioxide compressor running at 450 rev/min deals with 3 kg/min of the gas at 100°C, 10 bar. Determine the compressor swept volume if the volumetric efficiency is 73·2 per cent based on actual intake conditions.

If the volume delivered is 20 per cent of that taken in and the temperature is 220°C, what is the delivery pressure? (Use a generalised compressibility chart)   (406 cm³;   59·2 bar)

3.30 A gas at 266 K has a specific volume of $0 \cdot 0137 \text{ m}^3/\text{kg}$. It is compressed to 333 K where the specific volume is $0 \cdot 0106 \text{ m}^3/\text{kg}$. If the gas may be treated as obeying Van der Waals equation, derive expressions for the change of specific entropy and the change of specific internal energy and compute these values.

The value of c_v is constant at $0 \cdot 66 \text{ kJ/kg K}$, $a = 0 \cdot 182 \text{ kJ/kg}$, $b = 189 \times 10^{-6} \text{ m}^3/\text{kg}$, $R = 0 \cdot 189 \text{ kJ/kg K}$.

$$(0 \cdot 0989 \text{ kJ/kg K}, 40 \cdot 31 \text{ kJ/kg})$$

Solutions

3.1

The processes involved are shown on T–s and p–h diagrams in fig 3.1. For cooling (1)–(2) the energy equation for steady flow is

$$Q - W = h_2 - h_1 \quad \text{and} \quad W = 0$$

$$\therefore \quad Q = h_2 - h_1$$

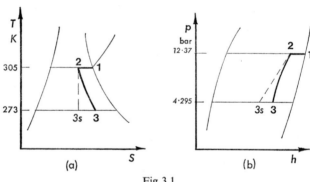

Fig 3.1

Taking data from the ammonia table

$$Q = 1469 \cdot 9 - 0 \cdot 2(1469 \cdot 9 - 332 \cdot 8) - 1469 \cdot 9 = -227 \cdot 42 \text{ kJ/kg}$$

$$s_2 - s_1 = s_g - (1 - x)(s_g - s_f) - s_1$$

and $$s_1 = s_g$$

$$\therefore \quad s_2 - s_1 = -0 \cdot 2(4 \cdot 962 - 1 \cdot 235) = \underline{-0 \cdot 7454 \text{ kJ/kg K}}$$

The second law postulates that the entropy of an *isolated* system cannot decrease. Our system is not isolated and there is a heat transfer *from* the system as indicated by the negative value of Q. This part of the process could be internally reversible when

$$\Delta s = \int_1^2 \frac{dQ}{T}$$

and since in this case p is constant and T is dependent on p because we are dealing with a saturated, two-phase mixture.

$$\Delta s = \frac{1}{T} \int_1^2 dQ = \frac{Q}{T} = -\frac{227 \cdot 42}{305} = -0 \cdot 7454 \text{ kJ/kg K as before.}$$

Consider next the isentropic* process (2)–(3s)

$$s_{3s} = s_2 = 4 \cdot 962 - 0 \cdot 7454 = 4 \cdot 2166 \text{ kJ/kg K}$$

But $\qquad s_{3s} = s_f + x(s_g - s_f)$

and $\qquad h_{3s} = h_f + x(h_g - h_f)$

$$= h_f + \left(\frac{s_{3s} - s_f}{s_g - s_f}\right)(h_g - h_f)$$

$$= 181 \cdot 2 + \left(\frac{4 \cdot 2166 - 0 \cdot 715}{5 \cdot 340 - 0 \cdot 715}\right)(1444 \cdot 4 - 181 \cdot 2)$$

$$= 1137 \cdot 4 \text{ kJ/kg}$$

$$\therefore \quad -\Delta h_s = h_2 - h_{3s} = 1242 \cdot 48 - 1137 \cdot 4 = 105 \cdot 08 \text{ kJ/kg}$$

Now the isentropic efficiency is defined as $\eta_s = \dfrac{\Delta h}{\Delta h_s}$

$$\therefore \quad -\Delta h = 105 \cdot 08 \times 0 \cdot 83 = 87 \cdot 2 \text{ kJ/kg}$$

$$\therefore \quad h_3 = 1155 \cdot 28 \text{ kJ/kg}$$

$$\therefore \quad x_3 = \frac{h_3 - h_f}{h_{fg}} = \underline{0 \cdot 771} \qquad \underline{\text{Final state}}$$

$$s_3 = s_f + x s_{fg} = 4 \cdot 2809 \text{ kJ/kg K}$$

$$s_3 - s_2 = 4 \cdot 2809 - 4 \cdot 2166 = \underline{0 \cdot 0643 \text{ kJ/kg K}}$$

* The term isentropic is used throughout to imply reversible isentropic which is therefore synonymous with reversible adiabatic. Thus all isentropic processes are regarded as adiabatic but only *reversible* adiabatics are isentropic.

For the expansion $Q = 0$

$$\therefore \quad -W = h_3 - h_2 = -87\cdot2 \text{ kJ/kg}$$

$$W = \underline{87\cdot2 \text{ kJ/kg}}$$

Note that the process (2)–(3) is irreversible, the entropy has increased although Q is zero.

3.2 The gas in this problem may be regarded as a simple compressible substance. That is, it has only one possible work mode of the form pdv. Hence its state can be influenced in only two ways, by work or heat. Two independent properties are sufficient to fix the state under these conditions and thus we may write the entropy as a function of internal energy and volume.

$$s = s\,(u, v)$$

$$ds = \left(\frac{\partial s}{\partial u}\right)_v du + \left(\frac{\partial s}{\partial v}\right)_u dv$$

but $\left(\dfrac{\partial s}{\partial u}\right)_v = \dfrac{1}{T}$ where T is the thermodynamic temperature and

$\left(\dfrac{\partial s}{\partial v}\right)_u = \dfrac{p}{T}$ where p is the thermodynamic pressure

$$\therefore \quad ds = \frac{du}{T} + \frac{pdv}{T}$$

The internal energy of a perfect gas is solely a function of T and

$$\frac{du}{dT} = c_v = \text{constant and } pv = RT$$

$$\therefore \quad ds = c_v\frac{dT}{T} + R\frac{dv}{v}$$

Integrating $\qquad s_2 - s_1 = c_v \ln \frac{T_2}{T_1} + R \ln \frac{v_2}{v_1} \qquad (1)$

For $N_2 \qquad R = \dfrac{R_0}{M} = \dfrac{8\cdot3143}{28} = 0\cdot297 \text{ kJ/kg K}$

$$T_2 = T_1\left(\frac{p_2}{p_1}\right)^{\frac{n-1}{n}} = 293\left(\frac{30}{1\cdot5}\right)^{\frac{0\cdot28}{1\cdot28}} = \underline{564 \text{ K}}$$

44

$$W = \int_{v_1}^{v_2} pdv = \frac{p_1v_1 - p_2v_2}{n-1} = \frac{mR(T_1 - T_2)}{n-1}$$

$$= \frac{2 \text{ kg} \times 0\cdot297 \text{ kJ/kg K} \times (-271) \text{ K}}{0\cdot28} = \underline{-575 \text{ kJ}}$$

$$\Delta U = mc_v\Delta T = m(c_p - R)\Delta T$$

$$= 2 \text{ kg} \times (1\cdot047 - 0\cdot297) \text{ kJ/kg K} (+271) \text{ K} = 406\cdot5 \text{ kJ}$$

Using the non-flow energy equation $Q - W = \Delta U$

$$Q = 406\cdot5 - 575 = \underline{-168\cdot5 \text{ kJ}}$$

Putting $\dfrac{v_2}{v_1} = \dfrac{p_1T_2}{p_2T_1}$ in equation (1) we have

$$s_2 - s_1 = c_v \ln \frac{T_2}{T_1} + (c_p - c_v) \ln \frac{p_1T_2}{p_2T_1}$$

$$s_2 - s_1 = c_p \ln \frac{T_2}{T_1} - R \ln \frac{p_2}{p_1}$$

$$= 1\cdot047 \text{ kJ/kg K} \ln \frac{564}{293} - 0\cdot297 \text{ kJ/kg K} \ln \frac{30}{1\cdot5}$$

$$= -0\cdot205 \text{ kJ/kg K}$$

$$S_2 - S_1 = -0\cdot205 \times 2 = \underline{-0\cdot410 \text{ kJ/K}}$$

3.3 $$Tds = du + pdv$$ (see example 3·2)

For the ideal gas $ds = c_v\dfrac{dT}{T} + R\dfrac{dv}{v}$

Now $$R = c_p - c_v = (a - b)$$

$$\therefore \quad ds = (b + kT)\frac{dT}{T} + (a - b)\frac{dv}{v}$$

$$\therefore \quad s_2 - s_1 = b \ln \frac{T_2}{T_1} + k(T_2 - T_1) + (a - b) \ln \frac{v_2}{v_1}$$

$$\frac{v_2}{v_1} = \frac{p_1T_2}{p_2T_1}$$

$$s_2 - s_1 = b \ln \frac{T_2}{T_1} + k(T_2 - T_1) + (a - b) \ln \frac{T_2}{T_1} - (a - b) \ln \frac{p_2}{p_1}$$

$$s_2 - s_1 = a \ln \frac{T_2}{T_1} + k(T_2 - T_1) - R \ln \frac{p_2}{p_1}$$

For the insentropic process described

$$0 = 1{\cdot}008 \ln \frac{T_2}{1400} + 2{\cdot}18 \times 10^{-4}(T_2 - 1400) - 0{\cdot}189 \ln \frac{1}{4} \quad (1)$$

This equation may be solved graphically or by trial.

As a first approximation assume the specific heats to be constant at the initial values.

$$c_p = 1{\cdot}313 \qquad c_v = 1{\cdot}124 \text{ kJ/kg K} \qquad \therefore \quad \gamma = \frac{c_p}{c_v} = 1{\cdot}168$$

With constant specific heats the gas is 'perfect' and the isentropic process will have the equation $pv^\gamma = $ constant.

hence $$T_2 = T_1 \left(\frac{p_2}{p_1}\right)^{\frac{\gamma-1}{\gamma}} = 1400\left(\frac{1}{4}\right)^{\frac{1}{6{\cdot}95}} = 1148 \text{ K}$$

In fact the specific heats will decrease during the expansion and the value of γ will increase since

$$c_v = \frac{R}{\gamma - 1}$$

The true value of T_2 will be less than 1148 K. Try values of T between 1150 and say 1100 K. Calculate $y = $ lefthand side of equation 1 and plot y against T then read off T for $y = 0$

Hence $T = 1140$ K

(The use of tables for u and h will be more accurate where these are available for the fluid concerned.)

Since the process is isentropic (reversible) it is also adiabatic, that is $Q = 0$.

$$W = m(h_2 - h_1) = mc_p(T_2 - T_1)$$

Where c_p is the mean specific heat since c_p varies linearly with temperature.

$$W = -5(1{\cdot}008 + 2{\cdot}18 \times 10^{-4} \times 1270)260 = \underline{-1670 \text{ kJ}}$$

Similarly the change of internal energy is given by

$$\Delta U = mc_v(T_2 - T_1) = -5(0{\cdot}819 + 2{\cdot}18 \times 10^{-4} \times 1270)260$$

$$= \underline{-1422 \text{ kJ}}$$

3.4

$$\psi = (h - h_0) - T_0(s - s_0) + \tfrac{1}{2}v^2 + g(z - z_0)$$

where subscript 0 refers to the surrounding state.

At (1) $\psi_1 = (h_1 - h_0) - T_0(s_1 - s_0)$ since KE and PE changes are negligible.

$$\therefore \quad \psi_1 = (3158 - 83\cdot9) \text{ kJ/kg} - 293 \text{ K } (6\cdot448 - 0\cdot296) \text{ kJ/kg K}$$

$$= \underline{1272\cdot1 \text{ kJ/kg}}.$$

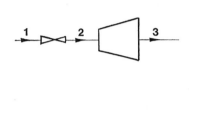

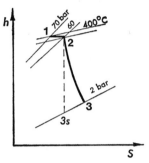

Fig 3.4

Note that h_0 and s_0 equal h_f and s_f respectively for water at 20°C. Since the pressure is 1·1 bar the water is subcooled (that is compressed liquid) but the effect on these properties is negligible.

At (2) $h_2 = h_1$ from the steady flow energy equation for adiabatic throttling.

Interpolating the superheat table at 60 bar for s at a known value of h (*viz* 3158 kJ/kg) we have $s_2 = 6\cdot512$ kJ/kg K

$$\psi_2 = (3158 - 83\cdot9) - 293(6\cdot512 - 0\cdot296) = \underline{1252\cdot8 \text{ kJ/kg}}$$

Note that the irreversible throttling operation has reduced the availability.

At (3s) after isentropic expansion, $s_{3s} = s_2 = 6\cdot512$ kJ/kg K

At 2 bar $s_g = 7\cdot127$ kJ/kg K thus the condition is wet.

$$h_{3s} = h_f + \left[\frac{s_{3s} - s_f}{s_{fg}}\right]h_{fg} = 2470 \text{ kJ/kg}$$

$$\therefore \quad \Delta h_s = 2470 - 3158 = -688 \text{ kJ/kg}$$

$$\Delta h = -688 \times 0\cdot82 = -564 \text{ kJ/kg}$$

$$h_3 = 2594 \text{ kJ/kg}$$

At 2 bar this enthalpy corresponds to an entropy of 6.830 kJ/kg K

$$\psi_3 = (2593 - 83.9) - 293(6.830 - 0.296) = \underline{595.7 \text{ kJ/kg}}$$

From the steady flow energy equation

$$-W = h_3 - h_2 = -564 \text{ kJ/kg}$$

$$\therefore \quad \text{Specific power} = \underline{564 \text{ kJ/kg}}$$

Note again that the loss of availability between points (2) and (3) exceeds the work done because of the irreversibility accounted for by the isentropic efficiency.

3.5 The non-flow availability is given by

$$\phi = (u - u_0) - T_0(s - s_0) + p_0(v - v_0)$$

$$\phi_1 - \phi_2 = (u_1 - u_2) - T_0(s_1 - s_2) + p_0(v_1 - v_2)$$

$$= c_v(T_1 - T_2) - T_0(s_1 - s_2) + p_0(v_1 - v_2)$$

$$T_2 = T_1\left[\frac{v_1}{v_2}\right]^{n-1} = 2773\left[\frac{1}{9}\right]^{0.38} = 1204 \text{ K}$$

$$s_2 - s_1 = c_v \ln\frac{T_2}{T_1} + R \ln\frac{v_2}{v_1} = -0.113 \text{ kJ/kg K}$$

$$v_1 = \frac{RT_1}{p_1} = 0.26 \frac{\text{kJ}}{\text{kg K}} \times 2773 \text{ K} \times \frac{1}{5800} \frac{\text{m}^2}{\text{kN}} \times 1 \frac{\text{m kN}}{\text{kJ}}$$

$$= 0.1243 \frac{\text{m}^3}{\text{kg}}$$

$$v_1 - v_2 = -8 \times 0.1243 = -0.9954 \frac{\text{m}^3}{\text{kg}}$$

$$\phi_1 - \phi_2 = 0.82(2773 - 1204) - 293 \times 0.113 + 110(-0.9954)$$
$$= \underline{1144 \text{ kJ/kg}}$$

$$W = \int_{v_1}^{v_2} p\,dv = \frac{p_1v_1 - p_2v_2}{n - 1} = \frac{mR(T_1 - T_2)}{n - 1} = \underline{1074 \text{ kJ/kg}}$$

From the non-flow energy equation $Q - W = \Delta u$

$$Q = c_v(T_2 - T_1) + W = \underline{-213 \text{ kJ/kg}}$$

3.6 The irreversibility $\qquad I = W_R - W \qquad$ (1)

where W_R is the reversible work between the same end states and W is the actual work. Using subscripts (1) and (2) for entry and exit respectively $\qquad W_R = (h_1 - h_2) - T_0(s_1 - s_2) \qquad$ (2)*

since KE changes are negligible.

The actual work W is obtainable from the adiabatic steady flow energy equation $\qquad -W = (h_2 - h_1) \qquad$ (3)

Substituting (2) and (3) in (1) $\quad I = -T_0(s_1 - s_2) = T_0(s_2 - s_1)$ (4)

Now $\qquad (s_2 - s_1) = c_p \ln \dfrac{T_2}{T_1} - R \ln \dfrac{p_2}{p_1}$

assuming that the air may be treated as a perfect gas.

$$s_2 - s_1 = 1{\cdot}005 \ln \frac{523}{294} - 0{\cdot}2871 \ln 6 = 0{\cdot}064 \text{ kJ/kg K}$$

$$I = 293(0{\cdot}064) = \underline{19 \text{ kJ/kg}}$$

Entropy production $= s_2 - s_1 - \dfrac{\dot{Q}}{T_0} = \underline{0{\cdot}064 \text{ kJ/kg K}}$ since $\dot{Q} = 0$

3.7†

For quasistatic expansion $W = \displaystyle\int_{V_1}^{V_2} p\,dv = \dfrac{p_1 V_1 - p_2 V_2}{n - 1}$

$$V_1 = mv_1 = 0{\cdot}2 \text{ kg} \times 0{\cdot}0151 \text{ m}^3/\text{kg} = 0{\cdot}00302 \text{ m}^3$$

$$V_2 = \left[\frac{p_1}{p_2}\right]^{\frac{1}{n}} V_1 = \left[\frac{13{\cdot}66}{6{\cdot}516}\right]^{1{\cdot}075} \times 0{\cdot}00302 = 0{\cdot}00671 \text{ m}^3$$

$$\therefore \quad W = 3{\cdot}43 \text{ kJ}$$

The non-flow energy equation gives $Q - W = \Delta U = U_2 - U_1$

$$U_2 - U_1 = m(h_2 - h_1) - (p_2 V_2 - p_1 V_1)$$

But $\qquad v_2 = \dfrac{0{\cdot}00671}{0{\cdot}2} = 0{\cdot}03355 \text{ m}^3/\text{kg}$

$$\therefore \quad (T_2 - T_{\text{sat}}) = \frac{0{\cdot}03355 - 0{\cdot}0269}{0{\cdot}0344 - 0{\cdot}0269} = 40 \text{ K}$$

* The term $(h - T_0 s) = b$, the Keenan availability function in steady flow. Thus $W_R = b_1 - b_2$.

† Solution of this problem would be facilitated by an enlarged SI table for Refrigerant 12 similar to BS 1725. The assumption that Charles' Law is obeyed by the superheated vapour produces appreciable errors in values of specific volume.

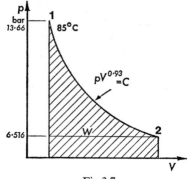

Fig 3.7

Extrapolating for h_2

$$h_2 = \frac{10}{15}(219\cdot11 - 208\cdot5) + 219\cdot11 = 226\cdot18 \text{ kJ/kg}$$

$$\therefore \quad \Delta U = 0\cdot2(226\cdot18 - 232\cdot42) - (651\cdot6 \times 0\cdot00671$$
$$- 1366 \times 0\cdot00302) = -1\cdot488 \text{ kJ}$$

$$\therefore \quad Q = -1\cdot488 + 3\cdot43 = 1\cdot942 \text{ kJ}$$

Entropy production $= \Delta s - \dfrac{Q}{T} \geq 0$

$$\Delta s = \frac{Q}{T_{MIN}}$$

$$T_{MIN} = \frac{Q}{\Delta S}$$

Extrapolating for s_2

$$s_2 = \frac{10}{15}(0\cdot7552 - 0\cdot7220) + 0\cdot7552 = 0\cdot7773 \text{ kJ/kg K}$$

$$s_1 = 0\cdot7496 \text{ kJ/kg K}$$

$$\therefore \quad \Delta S = 0\cdot0277 \times 0\cdot2 = 0\cdot00554 \text{ kJ/K}$$

$$\therefore \quad T_{MIN} = \frac{1\cdot942}{0\cdot00554} = 352 \text{ K or } \underline{79°C}$$

3.8

$$\psi_1 - \psi_2 = (h_1 - h_2) - T_0(s_1 - s_2) = c_p(T_1 - T_2) - T_0\left[c_p \ln \frac{T_1}{T_2}\right]$$

$$= 1\cdot08 \frac{\text{kJ}}{\text{kg K}}(100) \text{ K} - 293\left[1\cdot08 \ln \frac{800}{700}\right]\frac{\text{kJ}}{\text{kg}} = \underline{66 \text{ kJ/kg}}$$

Entropy production $= (S_2 + S_4) - (S_1 + S_3)$ since $Q = 0$ for the control volume shown.

$$\therefore \quad \text{Production} = (S_2 - S_1) + (S_4 - S_3)$$

$$= \left[-0.1435 + 2 \times 1.05 \ln \frac{T_4}{T_3} \right] \text{kJ/K kg exhaust (1)}$$

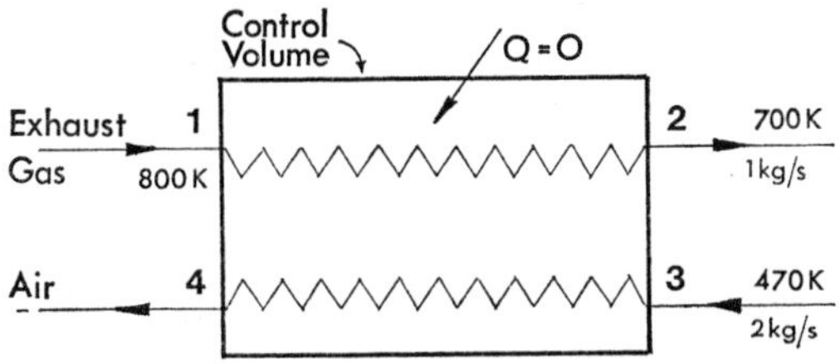

Fig 3.8

For each flow $Q = \Delta H$ from the steady flow energy equation.

$$\therefore \quad \Delta H_{\text{air}} = -\Delta H_{\text{exhaust}}$$

Now $\qquad 1.05(T_4 - 470) \times 2 = 1.08(800 - 700)$

$$\therefore \quad T_4 = 521.4 \text{ K}$$

Entropy production $= \underline{0.0731 \text{ kJ/K kg exhaust}}$ from (1)

Since this result is positive the scheme is feasible.

To make the process reversible, a reversible engine could be placed between the two fluids. In this case the entropy production would be zero.

Then $\qquad (S_2 - S_1) = (S_3 - S_4)$

$$-0.1435 = 1.05 \times 2 \ln \frac{470}{T_4}$$

whence $\qquad T_4 = 470 \times 1.0707 = 503 \text{ K}$

Now Q for exhaust $= -108$ kJ/kg exhaust

$\quad Q$ for air $= 2 \times 1.05 \times (503 - 470) = 69.3$ kJ/kg exhaust

$\quad W$ for reversible engine $= 108 - 69.3 = \underline{38.7 \text{ kJ/kg exhaust}}$

3.9
$$h \equiv u + pv \tag{1}$$

$$g \equiv h - Ts \tag{2}$$

$$f \equiv u - Ts \tag{3}$$

$$du = Tds - pdv \tag{4}$$

51

From (1) $$dh = du + pdv + vdp$$

$$\therefore \quad du = dh - pdv - vdp$$

Substituting in (4) gives $Tds = dh - vdp$

$$\therefore \quad dh = Tds + vdp \tag{5}$$

From (2) $$dg = dh - Tds - sdT$$

$$\therefore \quad dg = vdp - sdT \text{ by (5)} \tag{6}$$

From (3) and (4) $\quad df = du - Tds - sdT = -pdv - sdT \tag{7}$

Equations (4) to (7) are of the form $dz = Mdx + Ndy$
and since all the variables are thermodynamic properties

$$\left(\frac{\partial M}{\partial y}\right)_x = \left(\frac{\partial N}{\partial x}\right)_y$$

From (4) $$\left(\frac{\partial T}{\partial v}\right)_s = -\left(\frac{\partial p}{\partial s}\right)_v \tag{8}$$

From (5) $$\left(\frac{\partial T}{\partial p}\right)_s = \left(\frac{\partial v}{\partial s}\right)_p \tag{9}$$

Maxwell's Relations

From (6) $$\left(\frac{\partial v}{\partial T}\right)_p = -\left(\frac{\partial s}{\partial p}\right)_T \tag{10}$$

From (7) $$\left(\frac{\partial p}{\partial T}\right)_v = \left(\frac{\partial s}{\partial v}\right)_T \tag{11}$$

We require $$\left(\frac{\partial h}{\partial s}\right)_p$$

Now since for the simple substance only two properties are independent we may write $h = h(s, p)$

$$\therefore \quad dh = \left(\frac{\partial h}{\partial s}\right)_p ds + \left(\frac{\partial h}{\partial p}\right)_s dp$$

But $$dh = Tds + vdp \tag{5}$$

$$\therefore \quad T = \left(\frac{\partial h}{\partial s}\right)_p \text{ and } v = \left(\frac{\partial h}{\partial p}\right)_s$$

In the mixed phase region T and p are not independent. Hence if p is constant T is constant.

$$\therefore \quad \left(\frac{\partial h}{\partial s}\right)_p = \text{constant}$$

and the isobar is straight.

3.10

The reduced pressure $p_r = \dfrac{p}{p_c}$ where p_c is the critical pressure.

Similarly $v_r = \dfrac{v}{v_c}$ and $T_r = \dfrac{T}{T_c}$

$$\therefore \quad p = 2 \times 27\cdot 3 = \underline{54\cdot 6 \text{ bar}}$$

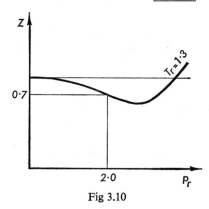

Fig 3.10

$$T = 1\cdot 3 \times 44\cdot 5 = \underline{57\cdot 85 \text{ K}}$$

$$pv = ZRT = Z\frac{R_0}{M}T \quad \text{and} \quad M = 20\cdot 183 \text{ kg/kg mole}$$

$$\therefore \quad v = \frac{0\cdot 7 \times 8\cdot 3143 \text{ kJ/kg mole K} \times 57\cdot 85 \text{ K}}{20\cdot 183 \text{ kg/kg mole} \times 5460 \text{ kN/m}^2}$$

$$= \underline{3\cdot 055 \times 10^{-3} \text{ m}^3/\text{kg}}$$

$$v_r = \frac{0\cdot 003055 \text{ m}^3/\text{kg} \times 20\cdot 183 \text{ kg/kg mole}}{0\cdot 0416 \text{ m}^3/\text{kg mole}} = \underline{1\cdot 482}$$

$$dh = Tds + vdp$$

$$s = s(p, T)$$

$$ds = \left(\frac{\partial s}{\partial p}\right)_T dp + \left(\frac{\partial s}{\partial T}\right)_p dT$$

But $\left(\dfrac{\partial s}{\partial p}\right)_T = -\left(\dfrac{\partial v}{\partial T}\right)_p$ see equation (10) of 3·9

$$\therefore \quad dh = T\left[-\left(\frac{\partial v}{\partial T}\right)_p dp + \left(\frac{\partial s}{\partial T}\right)_p dT\right] + vdp$$

Since for an isotherm $T =$ constant so that $dT = 0$

$$\therefore \quad dh_T = vdp - T\left(\frac{\partial v}{\partial T}\right)_p dp$$

Now
$$v = \frac{ZRT}{p}$$

$$\therefore \quad \left(\frac{\partial v}{\partial T}\right)_p = \frac{ZR}{p} + \frac{RT}{p}\left(\frac{\partial Z}{\partial T}\right)_p$$

and substituting for v

$$dh_T = ZRT\frac{dp}{p} - ZRT\frac{dp}{p} - RT^2\left(\frac{\partial Z}{\partial T}\right)_p \frac{dp}{p}$$

$$\therefore \quad dh_T = -RT^2\left(\frac{\partial Z}{\partial T}\right)_p \frac{dp}{p}$$

4

Non-reacting Mixtures

Questions

1. How do you compute the molecular mass of a mixture?

2. What is the significance of describing the constituents of a mixture as independent?

3. Write expressions for U, S, T, p and H of a mixture in terms of the corresponding values for its constituents.

4. Under what conditions is it reasonable to regard a mixture of water vapour and air as a mixture of independent perfect gases?

5. What happens to the system entropy when two constituents are allowed to mix in an isolated container?

6. A vessel is divided into two parts, each of which contains air at the same pressure and temperature. The vessel is isolated and the partition removed. Can anything be said about the entropy change of the whole system?

7. Define absolute and relative humidity.

8. Does a wet and dry bulb thermometer indicate the dew point?

9. Distinguish between the dew point and the adiabatic saturation temperature.

10. How many phases of a mixture of two constituents could exist together in equilibrium?

Worked Problems

4.1 The vacuum throughout the shell of a tubular steam condenser is 724 mmHg when the barometer stands at 760 mmHg. A group of tubes is screened off to form an air cooling section from which the air ejector draws. At entry to this section the temperature is 30°C and at the ejector suction it is 26°C. Calculate the mass of steam condensed in the section per hour and the ejector capacity in m^3/h if the air flow rate is 20 kg/h.

4.2 A laboratory has a volume of 470 m^3 and is to be kept at 20°C and a relative humidity of 52·5 per cent. The air in the room is to be completely changed once every hour and is drawn from atmosphere at 1·05 bar, 32°C, relative humidity 86 per cent, by a fan absorbing 450 W. This air passes through a cooler which reduces its temperature and causes condensation, the condensate being drained off at 8°C. The resulting saturated air is heated to room conditions. The total pressure is constant throughout the conditioner.

Determine (a) the temperature of the air leaving the cooler,
           (b) the condensation rate,
           (c) the heat transfer in the cooler,
           (d) the heat transfer in the heater.

4.3 Saturated air at 2°C is required to supply a room where the temperature must be held at 20°C with a relative humidity of 50 per cent. The air is heated and then water at 10°C is sprayed in to give the required humidity.

Determine the temperature to which the air must be heated and the mass of spray water required per m^3 of air at room conditions. Assume that the total pressure is constant at 1·02 bar and neglect the fan power.

4.4 Moist air having a relative humidity of 80 per cent at 30°C is cooled by spraying in water at 12°C. This causes saturation followed by condensation, the mixing being assumed to take place adiabatically and the condensate being drained off at 16·7°C. The resulting saturated mixture is then heated to produce the required conditions of 60 per cent relative humidity at 25°C. The total pressure is constant at 1·01 bar.

Determine the mass of water supplied to the sprays to provide 10^3 m^3/h of conditioned air. What heater power is required?

4.5 Water from a cooling system is itself to be cooled in a cooling tower at a rate of 10 000 kg/h. The water enters the tower at 65°C and leaves a collecting tank at the base at 30°C. Air flows through the tower entering the base at 15°C, 1·01 bar, 55 per cent relative humidity and leaving the top at 35°C, 1·01 bar, saturated. Make-up water enters the collecting tank at 14°C.

Determine the air flow rate into the tower in m^3/h and the make-up water flow rate in kg/h.

4.6 An evaporative condenser deals with 100 kg/min of Refrigerant 12 (CF_2Cl_2) which enters at 55°C, 6·516 bar and leaves at 20°C, 6·516 bar. Water feeds the cooling sprays at 18°C. Some of this water is evaporated into the air stream and the remainder at 25°C drains into a tank below the tubes where make-up water is added at 13°C before recirculation to the sprays. The air stream enters at 16°C with a relative humidity of 71 per cent and leaves saturated at 28°C, the atmospheric pressure being 1·005 bar.

Calculate the make-up flow rate and the spray flow rate.

4.7 A vessel is divided into three compartments (a), (b) and (c) by two partitions. Part (a) contains oxygen and has a volume of 0·1 m^3, (b) has a volume of 0·2 m^3 and contains nitrogen while (c) is 0·05 m^3 and holds CO_2. All three parts are at a pressure of 2·0 bar and a temperature of 13°C.

When the partitions are removed and the gases mix determine the change of entropy of each constituent, the final pressure in the vessel and the partial pressure of each gas. The vessel may be taken as completely isolated from its surroundings.

4.8 A trough containing octane (C_8H_{18}) liquid at 15°C is contained in a tube. Air flows through the tube entering at 15°C with a relative humidity of 60 per cent and leaving saturated with octane vapour at 10°C. The trough is kept at a fixed level by feeding in liquid octane at 15°C.

Determine the mixture composition by mass at exit and the heat transfer to the tube. The total pressure may be assumed to be constant throughout at 1·008 bar and kinetic energies are negligible. The enthalpy of formation of octane at 25°C is −250 000 kJ/kg mole for the liquid and −208 200 kJ/kg mole for the gas. The specific heats of the liquid and vapour are 2·225 and 1·66 kJ/kg K respectively. The vapour pressure at 10°C is 7·58 mbar. The effect of pressure on the enthalpies may be neglected.

4.9 An experiment is performed with methyl chloride (CH_3Cl) liquid in equilibrium with its vapour only from which it is found that the slope of the pressure-temperature curve obtained is 0·132 bar/K at 15°C. The latent enthalpy of methyl chloride at 15°C is found to be 388·2 kJ/kg. Working from fundamental state relations determine the change in specific volume during vaporisation.

4.10 A vessel contains carbon dioxide liquid and vapour at -20°C, 19·70 bar. If nitrogen is introduced until the pressure in the vessel rises to 40 bar, the temperature being kept constant, what will be the change in the saturation pressure of the carbon dioxide? Treat the CO_2 vapour as a perfect gas and assume that the liquid specific volume is constant at 0·001 m³/kg. The nitrogen and the carbon dioxide form an independent mixture.

Unworked Problems

4.11 Why are air cooling sections used in steam condensers? A condenser is to deal with 9000 kg/h of steam and 7 kg/h of air. The minimum steam temperature obtainable is 21°C and the steam temperature at the point of condensate extraction is 23°C.

Determine the capacity of the air ejectors, the mass of steam ejected with the air and the heat transfer rate in the air cooling section. Assume that the vacuum throughout the condenser shell is 734 mmHg when the barometer is 760 mmHg.

(602·9 m³/h, 11·05 kg/h, 5·51 kW)

4.12 Describe the salient features of large surface condensers for steam power plant.

The following data are available for a condenser having an air cooling section:

Vacuum throughout the shell (760 mmHg barometer) = 740 mmHg
Steam flow rate = 9060 kg/h
Air leakage = 8·6 kg/h
Temperature at entry to air cooling section = 20·4°C
Temperature at air pump suction = 15°C

Find (a) the mass of steam condensed per hour in the air cooling section and (b), the capacity of the air extraction plant in m³/h.

(38·2 kg/h, 739 m³/h)

4.13 A steady-flow air conditioning plant is to deal with an intake of 150 m³/min at 1·013 bar, 25°C and 75 per cent relative humidity. The delivery conditions are 1·013 bar, 20°C and 49 per cent relative humidity. Find the temperature to which the air must be cooled for dehumidification and the cooling and heating loads. Neglect the fan power and all losses and assume that the condensate discharges at saturation temperature.   (9°C, 103 kW, 32·4 kW)

4.14 An air conditioned room requires 30 m³/min of air at 1·013 bar, 20°C, 52·5 per cent relative humidity. The steady flow conditioner takes in air at 1·013 bar, 27°C, 77 per cent relative humidity which it cools to adjust the moisture content and reheats to room temperature. Find the temperature to which the air is cooled and the thermal loading on both cooler and heater. Assume that a fan before the cooler absorbs 0·5 kW and that the condensate is discharged at the temperature to which the air is cooled.   (10°C, 25 kW, 6·04 kW)

4.15 A room having a volume of 120 m³ is to be maintained at 17°C, 45 per cent relative humidity, the air being changed twice per hour. The external atmosphere is at 29°C, 88 per cent relative humidity. A fan absorbing 600 W blows air into the room via a cooler from which condensate is drained at the temperature of the air leaving the cooler. The air is then heated to room temperature, the pressure being 1·01 bar throughout.

Determine the heat transfer rates in the cooler and the heater.
                          (6·0 kW, 0·975 kW)

4.16 A grain dryer consists of a vertical cylindrical hopper through which hot air is blown. The air enters the base at 1·38 bar, 65°C, 50 per cent relative humidity. At the top saturated air is discharged to atmosphere at 1·035 bar, 60°C.

Estimate the moisture picked up by 1 kg of dry air and the total enthalpy change between the entering and leaving streams expressed per unit mass of dry air.   (0·0864 kg/kg air, 220 kJ/kg air)

4.17 An industrial process requires an atmosphere having a relative humidity of 88·4 per cent at 22°C and involves a flow rate of 2 × 10³ m³/h. The external conditions are 44·4 per cent relative humidity, 15°C. The air intake is heated and then humidified by water spray at 20°C. Determine the mass flow rate of spray water and the power required for heating if the pressure throughout is 1 bar.
                          (23·4 kg/h, 20·5 kW)

4.18 Atmospheric air at 1·005 bar, 1°C, 95 per cent relative humidity is to be conditioned for use in a room where the required temperature and humidity are 25°C and 45 per cent respectively. Determine the rate of heat transfer required prior to spraying in water at 6°C, if the intake of atmospheric air is 10 m³/s. What will be the rate of water flow to the sprays? Assume that the total pressure is constant throughout and neglect fan power. (470 kW, 64·5 g/s)

4.19 Air at a relative humidity of 90 per cent at 28°C enters a chamber where water is sprayed in at 14°C causing cooling and condensation. Heat transfer from the chamber is negligible and condensate is drained off at 15°C. The low temperature saturated air leaving the chamber is then heated to produce air at 22°C with 64·4 per cent relative humidity. The total pressure is 1·01 bar throughout and the conditioner delivers 100 m³/h of moist air.

Determine the heater power and the spray water flow rate.

(234 W, 1160 kg/h)

4·20 Cooling water enters a cooling tower at a rate of 1000 kg/h and 70°C. Water is pumped from the base of the tower at 24°C and some make-up is added afterwards. Air enters the tower at 15°C, 50 per cent relative humidity, 1·013 bar and is drawn from the tower saturated at 34°C, 1 bar. Determine the flow rate of the dry air in kg/h and the make-up water required per hour. (2088 kg/h, 62·9 kg/h)

4.21 In a refrigeration plant condensation of the ammonia used as the working fluid is caused by the evaporation of part of a water film from the outside of tubes through which the ammonia is flowing. The evaporation is assisted by blowing air across the tubes. This air enters at 1·017 bar, 15°C, 63 per cent relative humidity and leaves saturated at 22°C, 1·017 bar. Water enters at 18°C at a rate of 67 kg/min and leaves at 26°C. Ammonia enters at 11.67 bar, 130°C and leaves as saturated liquid at the same pressure. The flow rate of ammonia is 20 kg/min.

Calculate (a) the volume of air entering per minute and,

(b) the flow rate of make-up water required to be added prior to recirculation.

The fan power is to be neglected. (688 m³/min, 8·3 kg/min)

4.22 An evaporative cooler has a load of 300 kW. Water is pumped from a sump and supplied to the sprays that provide the cooling film at

15°C. The water drains into the collecting sump at 21°C. Make-up water is added to the sump at 14·5°C.

Air at 1·013 bar, 18°C, 42·2 per cent relative humidity is blown across the tube bank and leaves saturated at 1·013 bar, 23°C.

Find the make-up and spray water flow rates.

(0·104 kg/s, 0·112 kg/s)

4.23 The condenser shell of a refrigeration plant using Refrigerant 12 (CF_2Cl_2) has a net volume of 0·1 m^3. The refrigerant charge is pumped into the condenser and valves are closed to isolate it. When steady conditions are obtained the vessel is half filled with liquid and the pressure and temperature in the gas space are 7 bar and 25°C.

Determine the mass of air present.

If the mixture of refrigerant and air is homogeneous and is purged slowly to atmosphere until all the air is removed, how much liquid evaporates and how much work does the escaping mixture do against the atmospheric pressure of 1·01 bar. Assume that the temperature remains constant and that the evaporating refrigerant does not mix with the air-vapour mixture during the discharge. The specific volume of the liquid refrigerant at 25°C is 0·00076 m^3/kg.

(0·0283 kg, 1·912 kg, 35 kJ)

4.24 A gas cylinder has a volume of 0·8 m^3 and contains a mixture of carbon dioxide and nitrogen at a pressure of 2·0 bar and a temperature of 25°C, the total mass of the mixture being 2 kg. This cylinder is connected to another having a volume of 0·4 m^3 containing argon ($M = 40$) at 1·0 bar, 100°C. The combined system comes to equilibrium without heat transfer to the surroundings. Determine the final partial pressure of each gas and the total change in entropy during mixing.

Take $\gamma = 1·67$ for A, 1·23 for CO_2 and 1·4 for N_2 and treat the gases as perfect. (CO_2 0·25, N_2 1·11, A 0·27; 0·33 kJ/K)

4.25 A refrigerator containing some carbon dioxide is charged with ammonia. It is found that both fluids start condensing simultaneously at 20°C. Determine the mass ratio of ammonia to carbon dioxide and the total pressure when this occurs.

If a gas mixture in the same mass proportions were cooled whilst the total pressure was held constant at 25 bar, which fluid would start condensing first and what would be the mass of that fluid condensed before the other started to condense?

(0·0578, 65·87 bar, NH_3, 0·0181 kg NH_3/kg CO_2)

4.26 A simple carburettor is made by passing dry heated air across a reservoir of benzene (C_6H_6) the liquid level being maintained by a continuous supply at 15°C. The mixture has a mass ratio of 16:1 and a temperature of 15°C the benzene being completely vaporised. The total pressure throughout is 1·013 bar.

Find the temperature of the air supplied and the percentage saturation (relative 'humidity') of the mixture neglecting all heat transfer.

At 15°C the vapour pressure of C_6H_6 is 8·26 kN/m² and $h_{fg} =$ 33 800 kJ/kg mole.   (41·9°C, 27·9 per cent)

4.27 The table gives saturation pressures and temperatures of a fluid.

Sat Temp°C	0	5	10	15	20
Pressure bar	2·56	3·04	3·58	4·20	4·90

The liquid specific volume is sensibly constant over this range of temperature at 0·00106 m³/kg and the value of h_{fg} at 10°C is 393·9 kJ/kg.

Determine the specific volume and specific entropy of the saturated vapour at 10°C and the specific entropy of the liquid at 10°C. The arbitrary zero for entropy is −40°C and the liquid specific heat is 1·532 kJ/kg K.   (0·120 m³/kg, 1·689 kJ/kg K, 0·297 kJ/kg K)

4.28 Measurements on a fluid show that the changes of enthalpy and volume during vaporisation at −20°C are 284·0 kJ/kg and 0·01853 m³/kg respectively. It happens that this saturation temperature is close to that where the enthalpy of the vapour is a maximum, so that between −20 and −25°C h_g is virtually constant.

Estimate the change in saturation temperature resulting from a reduction in pressure of 1 bar. If the specific heat of the liquid is 2·04 kJ/kg K estimate the corresponding changes in the volume and enthalpy of vaporisation. The liquid volume may be assumed constant.   (−1·65 K;   0·000343 m³/kg;   3·37 kJ/kg)

4.29 The condenser of a laboratory refrigerator contains ammonia at 22°C. An investigator assumes that the saturation pressure in the condenser is given by the tabulated saturation pressure at 22°C. How much will he be in error if the vapour space contains an ammonia/air mixture in proportions 15:1 by mass and what is the total pressure in the vessel? ($v_f = 0·00165$ m³/kg at 22°C).

(0·042 per cent, 9·495 bar)

4.30 A chamber, volume 2 m³ contains air of relative humidity 36·9 per cent at 2°C. The pressure in the chamber is maintained at 1·013 bar by means of a large diaphragm. The chamber is then cooled. At what temperature will frost appear and what will the temperature be when 50 per cent of the moisture has been deposited? Find the heat transfer to cause this change.   (−10°C, −17°C, 53·6 kJ)

Solutions

4.1

760 mmHg = 1·01325 bar (see steam tables page 20)
724 mmHg Vacuum = (760 − 724) = 36 mmHg pressure

$$= \frac{1·01325}{760} \times 36 = 0·048 \text{ bar}$$

= pressure throughout shell

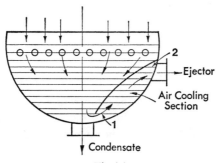

Fig 4.1

At point (1)
Temperature = 30°C $p_s = 0·04242$ bar from tables since the condition is saturated. (Condensation is occurring, both liquid and vapour are present.)
Now $p_s + p_a = p$ the pressure in the shell

$$\therefore \quad p_a = 0·048 − 0·04242 = 0·00558 \text{ bar} = 0·558 \text{ kN/m}^2$$

Consider a mass of mixture containing 1 kg of air. Its volume is v_{a_1} the specific volume of the air at point (1)

$$v_{a_1} = \frac{R_a T_1}{p_{a_1}} = \frac{0·2871 \times 303}{0·558} = 155·5 \text{ m}^3/\text{kg}$$

But volume of unit mass of steam = $v_{g_1} = 32·93 \text{ m}^3/\text{kg}$ and for the mixture, volume of steam = volume of air = volume of mixture

$$\therefore \quad \omega_1 = \frac{\text{mass steam}}{\text{mass air}} = \frac{v_{a1}}{v_{g1}} = 4 \cdot 72 \ \frac{\text{kg steam}}{\text{kg air}}$$

At point (2) temperature is 26°C, $p_s = 0 \cdot 0336$ bar

$$p_a = 0 \cdot 048 - 0 \cdot 0336 = 0 \cdot 0144 \text{ bar}$$

$$v_a = \frac{0 \cdot 2871 \times 299}{1 \cdot 44} = 59 \cdot 5 \text{ m}^3/\text{kg}$$

$$\therefore \quad \omega_2 = \frac{59 \cdot 5}{41 \cdot 03} = 1 \cdot 45 \ \frac{\text{kg steam}}{\text{kg air}}$$

Therefore mass condensed in the air cooling section

$$= 4 \cdot 72 - 1 \cdot 45 = 3 \cdot 27 \text{ kg/kg air}$$

mass/hour $= 3 \cdot 27 \times 20 = \underline{65 \cdot 4 \text{ kg/hour}}$

Volume to be dealt with by the ejector $= 20 \times v_{a2}$
$$= 20 \times 59 \cdot 5 = \underline{1190 \text{ m}^3/\text{h}}$$

4.2

The absolute humidity (*viz* the mass of steam per unit mass of dry air) does not change between points (2) and (3) and since the conditions at (2) are saturated, the temperature at (2) must be the saturation temperature corresponding to the partial pressure of the steam in the room, p_{s_3}, that is T_2 is the *dew point* of the room atmosphere.

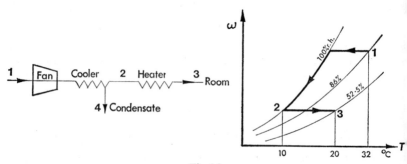

Fig 4.2

Now $\qquad p_{s_3} = $ relative humidity $\times (p_{sat} \equiv T_3)$

$$= 0 \cdot 525 \times 0 \cdot 02337 = 0 \cdot 01227 \text{ bar}$$

$$\therefore \quad T_2 = \underline{10°C} \qquad \qquad \text{(a)}$$

$$\text{The absolute humidity} = \frac{\text{mass steam}}{\text{mass air}} = \omega$$

Treating both fluids as perfect gases because the steam pressure is low we have

$$\omega = \frac{p_s V}{R_s T} \times \frac{R_a T}{p_a V} = \frac{R_a}{R_s} \times \frac{p_s}{p_a} = \frac{M_s}{M_a} \frac{p_s}{p_a}$$

$$= \frac{18}{28 \cdot 96} \times \frac{p_s}{p_a} = 0 \cdot 622 \frac{p_s}{p_a}$$

Now $\quad p_{a_3} = 1 \cdot 05 - 0 \cdot 01227 = 1 \cdot 03773 \text{ bar}$

$$\therefore \quad \omega_2 = \omega_3 = \frac{0 \cdot 622 \times 0 \cdot 01227}{1 \cdot 03773} = 0 \cdot 00736$$

At point (1) at $32°C$ $p_{s_1} = 0 \cdot 86 \times 0 \cdot 04754 = 0 \cdot 0408 \text{ bar}$

$$\therefore \quad p_{a_1} = 1 \cdot 05 - 0 \cdot 0408 = 1 \cdot 0092 \text{ bar}$$

$$\therefore \quad \omega_1 = \frac{0 \cdot 622 \times 0 \cdot 0408}{1 \cdot 0092} = 0 \cdot 0252$$

$\therefore \quad$ Condensate, $\omega_4 = \omega_1 - \omega_2 = 0 \cdot 01784 \text{ kg/kg air}$

Air flow rate $= \dfrac{p_{a_3} V}{R_a T_3}$

$$= 103 \cdot 772 \frac{\text{kN}}{\text{m}^2} \times 470 \frac{\text{m}^3}{\text{h}} \times \frac{1}{0 \cdot 2871} \frac{\text{kg K}}{\text{kN m}} \times \frac{1}{293 \text{ K}}$$

$$= 580 \text{ kg/h}$$

Condensate $= 580 \times 0 \cdot 01784 = \underline{10 \cdot 35 \text{ kg/h}}$ \hfill (b)

Applying the steady flow energy equation to the combined fan and heater and neglecting heat transfers in the fan we have

$$Q - W = H_2 + H_4 - H_1$$

$$\therefore \quad \dot{Q} = \dot{m}_a \left[\underset{\text{air}}{(h_2 - h_1)} + \underset{\text{water}}{(\omega_2 h_2 + \omega_4 h_4 - \omega_1 h_1)} \right] + W$$

$$= \dot{m}_a [c_{pa}(T_2 - T_1) + (\omega_2 h_2 + \omega_4 h_4 - \omega_1 h_1)] + W$$

$$= \frac{580}{3600} \frac{\text{kg}}{\text{s}} \left[1 \cdot 005 \frac{\text{kJ}}{\text{kg K}} (10 - 32) \text{ K} + (0 \cdot 00736 \times 2519 \cdot 2 \right.$$

$$\left. + \; 0 \cdot 01784 \; \times 33 \cdot 6 - 0 \cdot 0252 \times 2559 \cdot 3) \frac{\text{kJ}}{\text{kg}} \right] - 0 \cdot 45 \text{ kW}$$

(Note that h_1 is approximately h_g at 32°C since the effect of pressure on the enthalpy of superheated steam is small along an isotherm at low pressure.)

$$\therefore \quad \dot{Q} = -10.88 - 0.45 = \underline{-11.33 \text{ kW}} \quad \text{(c)}$$

Applying the steady flow energy equation to the heater we have

$$\dot{Q} = \dot{m}_a \left[c_{pa}(T_3 - T_2) + \omega_2 c_{ps}(T_3 - T_2) \right]$$

$$= \frac{580}{3600} \left[1.005 \times 10 + 0.00736 \times 1.86 \times 10 \right] = \underline{1.63 \text{ kW}} \quad \text{(d)}$$

Notes (1) c_{ps} from page 17 of tables
       (2) alternatively $\omega_2 c_{ps}(T_3 - T_2) = \omega_2(h_3 - h_2)$
       where $h_3 \simeq h_g$ at 20°C from tables.

4.3

At (1)
$$p_{s_1} = p_g \text{ at } 2°C = 0.007054 \text{ bar}$$

$$p_{a_1} = 1.02 - 0.007054 = 1.012946 \text{ bar}$$

$$\omega_1 = \frac{0.22 \times 0.007054}{1.012946} = 0.00432$$

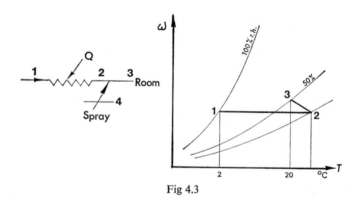

Fig 4.3

At (3)
$$p_{s_3} = 0.5 \times p_g \text{ at } 20°C$$

$$= 0.5 \times 0.02337 = 0.011685 \text{ bar}$$

$$p_{a_3} = 1.02 - 0.011685 = 1.008315 \text{ bar}$$

$$\omega_3 = \frac{0.622 \times 0.011685}{1.008315} = 0.0072$$

$$\therefore \quad \omega_3 - \omega_1 = 0.00288 \text{ kg/kg air}$$

$$v_{a_3} = \frac{R_a T_3}{p_{a_3}} = \frac{0.2871 \times 293}{100.8315} = 0.833 \text{ m}^3/\text{kg}$$

$$\text{Spray water} = \frac{0.00288}{0.833} = \underline{0.003457 \text{ kg/m}^3}$$

Applying the steady flow energy equation to a control surface through points (2), (3) and (4)

$$H_3 = H_2 + H_4$$

For unit mass of dry air

$$c_{pa}(T_3 - T_2) + \omega_3 h_3 - \omega_2 h_2 - (\omega_3 - \omega_1)h_4 = 0$$

$$\therefore \quad 1.005(20 - T_2) + 0.0072 \times 2537.6 - 0.00432\, h_2$$
$$- 0.00288 \times 42 = 0$$

For the low pressure superheated steam at (2) we may write

$$h_2 = h_1 + c_p(T_2 - T_1) = 2504.3 + 1.86(T_2 - 2)$$

Making this substitution we may solve for T_2

$$T_2 = \underline{27.1°C}$$

.4

$$p_{s_1} = 0.8 \times 0.04242 = 0.03394 \text{ bar}$$

$$p_{a_1} = 1.01 - 0.03394 = 0.97606 \text{ bar}$$

$$\omega_1 = 0.622 \times \frac{0.03394}{0.97606} = 0.02161$$

$$p_{s_4} = 0.6 \times 0.03166 = 0.0190 \text{ bar} \equiv \text{Saturation temperature of } 16.7°C$$

$$p_{a_4} = 1.01 - 0.0190 = 0.991 \text{ bar}$$

$$\omega_4 = 0.622 \times \frac{0.019}{0.991} = 0.01192 = \omega_3$$

A mass balance on the spray chamber yields, for unit mass of air

$$\dot{m}_5 + \omega_3 = \omega_1 + \dot{m}_6 \qquad (i)$$

The energy equation gives

$$c_p(T_3 - T_1) + \omega_3 h_3 + \dot{m}_5 h_5 - \omega_1 h_1 - \dot{m}_6 h_6 = 0 \quad (ii$$

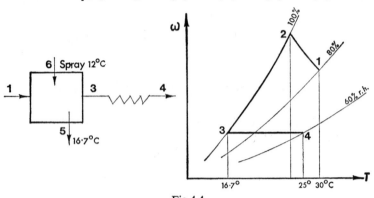

Fig 4.4

from (ii)

$$1{\cdot}005(16{\cdot}7 - 30) + 0{\cdot}01192 \times 2546{\cdot}6 + \dot{m}_5 70$$
$$- 0{\cdot}02161 \times 2555{\cdot}7 - \dot{m}_6 50{\cdot}4 = ($$

$$\therefore \quad -38{\cdot}1665 + 70\dot{m}_5 - 50{\cdot}4\dot{m}_6 = 0$$

from (i)

$$\dot{m}_5 + 0{\cdot}01192 = 0{\cdot}02161 + \dot{m}_6$$

$$\dot{m}_5 = 0{\cdot}00969 + \dot{m}_6$$

Hence $\quad -38{\cdot}1665 + 70(0{\cdot}00969 + \dot{m}_6) - 50{\cdot}4\dot{m}_6 = 0$

$$\therefore \quad \dot{m}_6 = 1{\cdot}915 \text{ kg/kg air}$$

$$v_{a_4} = \frac{R_a T_4}{p_{a_4}} = \frac{0{\cdot}2871 \times 298}{99{\cdot}1} = 0{\cdot}863 \text{ m}^3\text{/kg}$$

$$\dot{m}_a = \frac{10^3 \text{ m}^3\text{/h}}{0{\cdot}863 \text{ m}^3\text{/kg}} = 1159 \text{ kg/h}$$

$$\therefore \quad \text{Spray water} = 1{\cdot}915 \times 1159 = \underline{2224 \text{ kg/h}}$$

For the heater the energy equation gives

$$Q = \dot{m}_a[c_{p_a}(T_4 - T_3) + \omega_3 c_{p\text{H}_2\text{O}}(T_4 - T_3)]$$

$$= 1159[1{\cdot}005 \times 8{\cdot}3 + 0{\cdot}01192 \times 1{\cdot}86 \times 8{\cdot}3] = 9860 \text{ kJ/h}$$
$$= \underline{2{\cdot}75 \text{ kW}}$$

4.5

$$p_{s_1} = 0.55 \times 0.01704 = 0.009372 \text{ bar}$$

$$p_{a_1} = 1.01 - 0.009372 = 1.000\ 28 \text{ bar}$$

$$\omega_1 = \frac{0.622 \times 0.009372}{1.000628} = 0.00579$$

$$p_{s_2} = 0.05629 \qquad p_{a_2} = 0.95371 \text{ bar}$$

$$\omega_2 = 0.0367$$

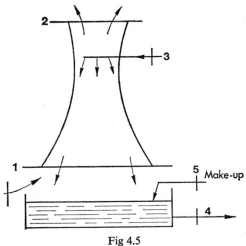

Fig 4.5

Make-up $= \omega_2 - \omega_1 = 0.03091$ kg/kg air

Energy balance gives $H_2 + H_4 - H_1 - H_3 - H_5 = 0$

For 1 kg air

$$c_{p_a}(T_2 - T_1) + \omega_2 h_2 - \omega_1 h_1 + \dot{m}_w(h_4 - h_3) - 0.02951\, h_5 = 0$$

$$1.005 \times 20 + 0.0367 \times 2564.7 - 0.00579 \times 2528.4$$
$$+ \dot{m}_w(-146.3) - 0.03091 \times 58.8 = 0$$

$$\therefore \quad \dot{m}_w = 0.668 \text{ kg/kg air}$$

$$\dot{m}_a = \frac{10\ 000}{0.668} = 14\ 950 \text{ kg/h}$$

$$\text{Air flow} = \frac{14\ 950 \times 0.2871 \times 288}{1.000628 \times 10^2} = \underline{12\ 350 \text{ m}^3/\text{h}}$$

Make-up $= 0.03091 \times 14\ 950 = \underline{159 \text{ kg/h}}$

4.6

$$p_{s_3} = 0.71 \times p_s \text{ at } 16°C = 0.71 \times 0.01817 = 0.0129 \text{ bar}$$

$$p_{a_3} = 1.005 - 0.0129 = 0.9921 \text{ bar}$$

$$\omega_3 = \frac{0.622 \times 0.0129}{0.9921} = 0.0081$$

$$p_{s_4} = 0.03778 \text{ bar} \qquad p_{a_4} = 0.96722 \text{ bar}$$

$$\omega_4 = 0.0243$$

$\therefore$ Make-up required $= \omega_4 - \omega_3 = 0.0162$ kg/kg air.

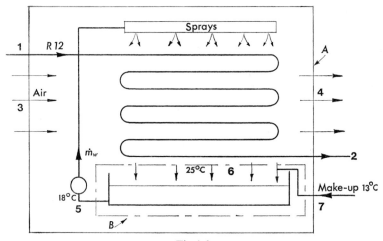

Fig 4.6

Considering the control volume (A)

$$(H_2 + H_4) - (H_1 + H_3 + H_7) = 0$$

$$\therefore \quad H_2 - H_1 + H_4 - H_3 - H_7 = 0$$

$\therefore \quad \dot{m}_{R12}(h_2 - h_1) + \dot{m}_a[c_{pa}(T_4 - T_3) + \omega_4 h_4 - \omega_3 h_3$

$$- (\omega_4 - \omega_3)h_7] = [100(54.87 - 219.11) + \dot{m}_a(1.005 \times 12$$

$$+ 0.0243 \times 2552.1 - 0.0081 \times 2530.2 - 0.0162$$

$$\times 54.6)] \text{ kJ/min} = 0$$

Whence $\dot{m}_a = 312$ kg/min

Make-up flow rate $= 312 \times 0.0162 = \underline{5.05 \text{ kg/min}}$

Considering the control volume (B)

$$H_5 - H_6 - H_7 = 0$$

$$\dot{m}_w 75 \cdot 5 - (\dot{m}_w - 5 \cdot 05)104 \cdot 8 - 5 \cdot 05 \times 54 \cdot 6 = 0$$

$$\dot{m}_w = \underline{8 \cdot 64 \text{ kg/min}}$$

4.7 Consider any constituent i and denote the conditions prior to mixing by subscript 1 and after mixing by subscript 2.

Then
$$p_{i_1} V_{i_1} = n_i R_0 T_1 \qquad (i)$$

$$p_{i_2} V_{i_2} = n_i R_0 T_2 \qquad (ii)$$

Since the internal energy is constant because of the isolation $T_1 = T_2$ and dividing (ii) by (i)

$$\frac{p_{i_2} V_{i_2}}{p_{i_1} V_{i_1}} = 1$$

$$\therefore \quad \frac{p_{i_2}}{p_{i_1}} = \frac{V_{i_1}}{V_{i_2}} = \frac{V_{i_1}}{V} = \frac{n_i}{n} = x_i$$

where V is the volume of the vessel, that is the volume of the mixture.

But
$$\frac{p_{i_2}}{p_2} = \frac{V_i}{V} = \frac{n_i}{n} = x_i \qquad (iii)$$

where p_2 is the total pressure of the mixture.

Hence $p_{i_1} = p_2$ and there is no change in the pressure in the vessel

$$\therefore \quad p_2 = \underline{2.0 \text{ bar.}}$$

From (iii) $p_{i_2} = x_i p_2$

$$\therefore \quad \text{for oxygen} \quad p_2 = \frac{2 \times 0 \cdot 1}{0 \cdot 35} = \underline{0 \cdot 5714 \text{ bar}}$$

$$\text{nitrogen} \quad p_2 = \frac{2 \times 0 \cdot 2}{0 \cdot 35} = \underline{1 \cdot 1429 \text{ bar}}$$

$$CO_2 \quad p_2 = \frac{2 \times 0 \cdot 05}{0 \cdot 35} = \underline{0 \cdot 2857 \text{ bar}}$$

$$\Delta S_i = n_i \left[c_{vi} \ln \frac{T_2}{T_1} + R_0 \ln \left(\frac{V_{i_2}}{V_{i_1}} \right) \right]$$

$$= n_i R_0 \ln\left(\frac{V_{i_2}}{V_{i_1}}\right) \text{ for constant temperature}$$

$$= \frac{p_{i_1} V_{i_1}}{T} \ln\left(\frac{V_{i_2}}{V_{i_1}}\right)$$

For oxygen $\Delta S = \dfrac{200 \times 0 \cdot 1}{286} \ln \dfrac{0 \cdot 35}{0 \cdot 1} = \underline{0 \cdot 0876 \text{ kJ/K}}$

Similarly for nitrogen $\Delta S = \underline{0 \cdot 0783 \text{ kJ/K}}$

for CO_2 $\quad \Delta S = \underline{0 \cdot 0680 \text{ kJ/K}}$

4.8

The mass of steam per unit mass of air

$$= \omega_s = \frac{p_s M_s}{p_a M_a} = 0 \cdot 622 \frac{p_s}{p_a}$$

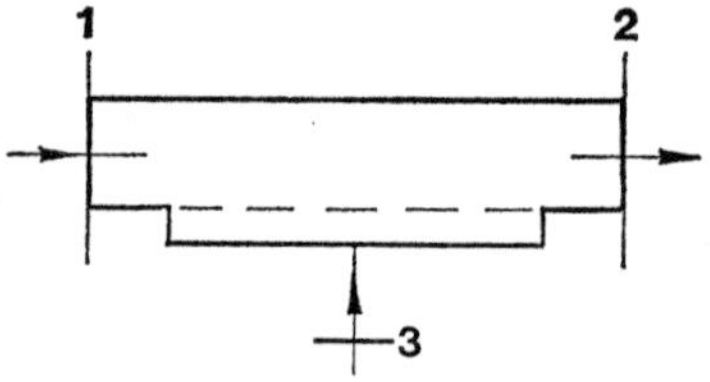

Fig 4.8

Since no water is added or removed from the control volume and assuming that no condensation occurs $\omega_{s1} = \omega_{s2} = \omega_s$

Similarly $\qquad \dfrac{m_{octane}}{m_a} = \omega_{octane} = \dfrac{p_{oct} M_{oct}}{p_a M_a}$

Since there is no octane at plane (1)

$$\omega_s = \frac{0 \cdot 622 \, p_{s1}}{1 \cdot 008 - p_{s1}} \text{ where } p_{s1} = 0 \cdot 6 \, p_{sat} = 0 \cdot 6 \times 0 \cdot 01704 = 0 \cdot 010224 \text{ bar}$$

$$\therefore \quad \omega_s = 0 \cdot 00637$$

At section (2) the air is saturated with octane and the partial pressure of the octane is $7 \cdot 58$ mbar

$$p_{s2} = \frac{\omega_s p_{a2}}{0 \cdot 622}$$

$$p_{a2} = 1 \cdot 008 - 0 \cdot 00758 - p_{s2} \qquad \therefore \quad p_{s2} = 0 \cdot 01014 \text{ bar}$$

But $p_{sat_2} = 0.01227$ bar and since this is greater than p_{s2} our assumption of no condensation is correct.

$$p_{a2} = 1.008 - 0.00758 - 0.01014 = 0.99028 \text{ bar}$$

$$\omega_{oct} = \frac{114 \times 0.00758}{28.96 \times 0.99028} = 0.0313$$

So the mixture composition at exit is

1 kg air, 0.0313 kg octane, 0.00637 kg water.

Using the steady flow energy equation we have

$$Q = (h_{a2} - h_{a1}) + \omega_s(h_{s2} - h_{s1}) + (\omega h)_{oct_2} - (\omega h)_{oct_3}$$

$$h_{oct_3} = \frac{1}{M}(\text{enthalpy of formation at 25°C in kJ/mole}) - c_p (25 - T_3)$$

$$= -\frac{250\,000}{114} - 2.25 \times 10 = -2217.5 \text{ kJ/kg}$$

Similarly $\qquad h_{oct_2} = -1854.1 \text{ kJ/kg}$

$$\therefore \quad Q = 1.005(-5) + 0.00637(2519.2 - 2528.4)$$
$$+ 0.0313(-1854.1 + 2217.5)$$
$$= \underline{6.31 \text{ kJ/kg air}}$$

4.9 The specific Gibbs function g is defined by $g = h - Ts$

$$\therefore \quad dg = dh - Tds - sdT$$

But $\qquad\qquad Tds = dh - vdp$

$$\therefore \quad dg = vdp - sdT$$

Across the two-phase mixture state both T and p can be held constant.

$$dg = 0 \quad \text{and} \quad g_f = g_g$$

Also for a change in saturation pressure dp, $\quad dg_f = dg_g$

$$\therefore \quad v_f dp - s_f dT = v_g dp - s_g dT$$

$$\therefore \quad (v_g - v_f)dp = (s_g - s_f)dT$$

$$\therefore \quad \frac{dp}{dT_{sat}} = \frac{s_{fg}}{v_{fg}} = \frac{h_{fg}}{T_{sat}v_{fg}} \quad \text{Clapeyron's Equation}$$

For methyl chloride at 15°C we have

$$0.132 \times 10^2 \, \frac{kN}{m^2 K} = \frac{388.2 \text{ kJ/kg}}{288 \text{ K } v_{fg}}$$

$$\therefore \quad \underline{v_{fg} = 0.102 \text{ m}^3/\text{kg}}$$

4.10 The equilibrium condition between the CO_2 liquid and vapour requires that the chemical potential of each phase is the same.

$$\mu_f = \mu_g$$

Since the mixture is independent

$$g_f = g_g$$

g_f will be a function of the total pressure on the liquid but g_g will depend on the partial pressure of the carbon dioxide.

$$\therefore \quad \left(\frac{\partial g_f}{\partial p}\right)_T dp = \left(\frac{\partial g_g}{\partial p_g}\right)_T dp_g$$

now $$dg = vdp - sdT \quad \text{(see **4.9**)}$$

$$\therefore \quad \left(\frac{\partial g}{\partial p}\right)_T = v$$

$$\therefore \quad dp_g = \frac{v_f dp}{v_g}$$

Putting $$v_g = \frac{RT}{p_g} \qquad dp_g = \frac{v_f p_g dp}{RT} \quad \text{or} \quad \frac{dp_g}{p_g} = \frac{v_f dp}{RT}$$

Integrating $$\ln \frac{p_{g2}}{p_{g1}} = \frac{v_f}{RT}(p_2 - p_1)$$

$$= \frac{0.001 \times 44}{8.3143 \times 253}(4000 - 1970)$$

$$= 0.04246$$

$$\frac{p_{g2}}{p_{g1}} = 1.0434 \qquad \underline{p_{g2} = 20.55 \text{ bar}}$$

5

Combustion

Questions

1. Can an absolute zero of energy be defined?

2. Can an absolute zero of entropy be defined?

3. What arbitrary datum is used for energy in chemical reactions?

4. Define enthalpy of combustion and internal energy of combustion.

5. How are the two quantities defined in (4) related?

6. Define enthalpy and internal energy of formation of a compound.

7. The enthalpy of combustion of CH_4 at 298 K is given in the tables as $-802\ 300$ kJ/kg mole. What does the negative sign imply?

8. What is the relation between calorific value and enthalpy of combustion?

9. Distinguish between the gross and net calorific values of a hydrocarbon fuel.

10. How would you fix the equilibrium condition for a reaction at constant pressure and temperature?

Worked Problems

5.1 Nonane, C_9H_{20}, is burned with (a) the minimum air for complete combustion (that is the stoichiometric mixture); (b) 20 per cent excess air; (c) 80 per cent of the stoichiometric air. Find the air-fuel ratio by mass and the analysis of the total products of the combustion by volume for each case.

5.2 A gaseous fuel has the following percentage volumetric analysis: O_2 0·4, CO_2 4·0, C_4H_8 2·0, CH_4 20·0, CO 18·0, H_2 49·4 and N_2 6·2. Determine the stoichiometric air-fuel ratio by volume and produce an expression for the volumetric air-fuel ratio in non-stoichiometric combustion in terms of the percentage of CO_2 in the dry products of combustion.

5.3 A liquid fuel has an ultimate mass analysis of 86·2 per cent carbon, 13·8 per cent hydrogen. The volumetric analysis of the dry exhaust gas from an engine using this fuel is CO_2 9·8 per cent, O_2 8·1 per cent, N_2 82·1 per cent. Determine the air-fuel ratio by mass.

5.4 The enthalpy of combustion of liquid decane, $C_{10}H_{22}$, at 25°C is $-47·450$ MJ/kg with liquid H_2O in the products. Determine the internal energy of combustion (a) under the same conditions, (b) when there is vapour H_2O in the products.

5.5 A fully vaporised stoichiometric mixture of octane, C_8H_{18}, and air is supplied to a combustion device at 25°C and the products of combustion leave at 200°C. Compute the heat transfer during the combustion process. Take mean values of specific heats from the tables.

5.6 Calculate the adiabatic flame temperature for a mixture of benzene vapour C_6H_6, with 120 per cent of the stoichiometric air at 25°C. What is the effect on this temperature of replacing 20 per cent of the nitrogen by an equal mass of additional oxygen?

5.7 The oil fuel supplied to a boiler has an ultimate mass analysis H_2 16 per cent, C 84 per cent, its flow rate is 115 kg/h and its gross calorific value 45·3 MJ/kg. The volumetric analysis of the dry flue gases is 9·8 per cent CO_2, 7·42 per cent O_2 and 82·8 per cent N_2.

Feed water is supplied at 50°C, the boiler room temperature is 25°C and 1500 kg/h of steam is generated at 20 bar with a dryness fraction of 0·98. The flue gas has a temperature of 327°C. Determine the efficiency of the boiler and draw up an energy account.

5.8 A six-cylinder water cooled Diesel engine develops 110 kW at 2600 rev/min with a specific fuel consumption of 0·245 kg/kWh. The fuel has an ultimate analysis of 86 per cent C, 14 per cent H_2 and a gross calorific value of 44 MJ/kg. The dry exhaust gas contains 8·9 per cent CO_2 but no CO and the exhaust temperature is 377°C. The cooling water flow rate is 60 kg/min with a temperature rise of 24 K. Determine the thermal efficiency of the engine and make an energy distribution analysis based on an air intake temperature of 25°C.

5.9 (a) Hydrogen exists in equilibrium at 3000 K, 2 bar. Determine the mole fractions of H and H_2 present using the data on page 18 of the Mayhew and Rogers Tables.

(b) A mixture of CO, H_2O, CO_2 and H_2 exists in equilibrium at a pressure of 20 atmospheres. The volumetric analysis of the mixture is 10 per cent CO, 55·4 per cent H_2O, 24·6 per cent CO_2 and 10 per cent H_2. Determine the mixture temperature.

5.10 The mixture in a petrol engine may be assumed to be a 20 per cent rich mixture of octane, C_8H_{18}, and air which is burned at constant volume. The conditions at the beginning of combustion are 18·4 bar 680 K. The products of combustion contain CO_2, CO, H_2O, H_2, O_2 and N_2 and the maximum temperature reached is 2700 K. Show that approximately 41·5 per cent of the carbon has been burned to CO instead of CO_2.

Unworked Problems

5.11 Give a brief description of the Orsat apparatus for the analysis of engine exhaust gases.

A fuel has an ultimate mass analysis of 89·3 per cent C, 5 per cent H_2, 1·5 per cent N_2 and 4·2 per cent O_2. What is the percentage volumetric composition of the products from stoichiometric combustion, including vapour?

(17·66 per cent CO_2, 76·4 per cent N_2, 5·94 per cent H_2O)

5.12 A gas-fired water heater may be treated as a steady flow system in which 0·23 kg/min of water is heated from 13·5 to 60°C. The gas burned may be regarded as C_4H_{10} and has a gross calorific value of 117·5 MJ/m³ at 25°C, 1·013 bar.

Determine the flow rates of air and gas when the mixture strength is 90 per cent of the stoichiometric value and the heater efficiency is 80 per cent. Both air and gas are supplied at 25°C, 1·013 bar and the products of combustion leave at 25°C.

(16·32 and 0·475 litres/min)

5.13 Describe a method of measuring the calorific value of an oil fuel. A fuel has an ultimate mass analysis of 59.5 per cent C, 11·6 per cent

H_2 and 28·9 per cent O_2. Determine (a) the stoichiometric air-fuel ratio, (b) the volumetric analysis of the dry products of combustion when the mixture is 20 per cent rich.

(9·56; 9·9 per cent CO_2, 8·56 per cent CO, 81·54 per cent N_2)

5.14 Define calorific value and explain briefly how it may be evaluated for a liquid fuel.

During a test to determine the calorific value of coal gas it was observed that during a period of 4·5 minutes:

    volume of gas burned   = 9·7 litres at 76 cmHg, 25°C.
    mass of water heated   = 2150 g.
    temperature rise of water = 20·3 K

During a period of 1 hour 69 g of condensate were collected. Ca)-culate the gross and the net calorific values.

(18 800, 17 500 kJ/m³)

5.15 The mass analysis of a coal used in a boiler is 82 per cent C, 8 per cent H_2, 3 per cent O_2 and 7 per cent ash. The fuel consumption is 1330 kg/h, the air for combustion being supplied by a fan so that it is 30 per cent in excess of the stoichiometric.

Find (a) the composition by volume of the wet products of combustion and (b) the volume of air at 1·02 bar, 18°C taken in by the fan per minute.

(12·14 per cent CO_2, 7·12 per cent H_2O, 4·64 per cent O_2, 76·1 per cent N_2; 282 m³/min.)

5.16 An automatic oil fired boiler uses 100 kg/h of fuel oil of mass analysis 84 per cent C, 14 per cent H_2, and gross calorific value 45·5 MJ/kg. The air consumption is 31 m³/min measured at 27°C, 1·013 bar. The steam flow rate is 1300 kg/h at 11 bar, 0·96 dry, raised from feed water at 55°C. The flue gas temperature is 300°C.

Determine the boiler efficiency and the enthalpy of the dry flue gas and of the vapour in the flue, measured above the inlet air temperature of 27°C. Take c_p for dry flue gas as 1·005 kJ/kg K.

(70·6 per cent; 165 kW; 103·6 kW)

5.17 What is the effect of high latent enthalpy of vaporisation of a fuel on the design and performance of a spark-ignition engine?

Gaseous dodecane, $C_{12}H_{26}$, is burned with 120 per cent of the stoichiometric air in a steady flow process at 25°C. At this temperature the enthalpy of combustion of liquid dodecane is -47.5 MJ/kg and the latent enthalpy of vaporisation is 358 kJ/kg. Find the constant pressure and constant volume gross calorific values of 1 litre of the mixture at 25°C, 1·013 bar.   (3·107, 3·095 kJ/litre)

5.18 A mixture of air and octane vapour, C_8H_{18}, mass ratio 50:1 is burned in a steady flow constant pressure combustion chamber from which the heat loss is negligible. If the mixture enters at 37°C, calculate the analysis of the products and show that their temperature is approximately 1080 K. Neglect dissociation.

5.19 Acetylene, C_2H_2, is burned with 30 per cent excess air in an iso-thermal, isobaric process at 25°C and 1 atmosphere pressure. What is the heat transfer per kg C_2H_2 if the water in the products is liquid? Use the following standardised enthalpies at 25°C:

$$C_2H_2 \ 227·2, \quad CO_2 \ -393, \quad H_2O \ -286·2 \ \text{MJ/kg mole}$$

If the temperature of the reactants were increased to 400 K, other conditions being unchanged, what would be the change in heat transfer?

c_p for C_2H_2 is 39·7 kJ/kg mole K;

c_p for diatomics 33·6 kJ/kg mole K
     (-50 MJ/kg; $-2·19$ MJ/kg)

5.20 A gas bottle contains 6 kg of saturated liquid butane, C_4H_{10}, at 21°C and a negligible mass of vapour. The bottle is connected via a restrictor to a heating unit where combustion takes place at a constant pressure of 1·01 bar, the products leaving at 200°C. The air supply is 20 per cent in excess of the stoichiometric and the butane vapour enters the burner at the rate of 68 litres/hour and 21°C.

Determine (a) the air consumption,

           (b) the rate of heat transfer in the heater neglecting all losses,

           (c) the time to use the available butane,

           (d) the rate of heat transfer to the bottle.

For saturated C_4H_{10} at 21°C, 2·16 bar, $h_{fg} = 365$ kJ/kg,

$$v_f = 1·7 \ \text{litres/kg}, \quad v_g = 183 \ \text{litres/kg}.$$

For C_4H_{10} vapour at 1·01 bar, 21°C v = 0·405 m^3/kg.

The enthalpy of combustion of butane at 21°C is −2880 MJ/kg mole

(2·6 m^3/h; 2·14 kW from butane; 35·7 h; 17 W

5.21 A gas fuel containing CO, H_2 and N_2 only, is produced by passin
air and steam through incandescent carbon. Use the reaction dat
given in the Mayhew and Rogers tables to calculate the volumetri
analysis of the gas, its net calorific value in kJ/m^3 at 25°C, 1 atm
and the efficiency of the process.

(40·4 per cent CO, 18·4 per cent H_2, 41·4 per cent N_2
6500 kJ; 94·6 per cen

5.22 A steam generator produces 1500 kg/h of steam at 18 bar with
dryness fraction of 0·98 from feed water at 50°C. The air intake is a
1·013 bar, 25°C and has a relative humidity of 82 per cent. Th
analysis of a sample of the dry flue gases shows 10 per cent CO
The flue gas temperature is 277°C. The fuel consumption is 110 kg/
using oil of gross calorific value 45·4 MJ/kg and a mass analysi
14 per cent H_2, 86 per cent C. Determine the boiler efficiency an
the percentage of the fuel energy contained in (a) the dry flue gase
and (b) the flue vapour.

(76·7 per cent; 12·2 per cent; 10·4 per cen

5.23 The fuel used in a petrol engine may be regarded as heptane, C_7H_{16}
and a rich mixture produced a dry exhaust of analysis 8·8 per cen
CO_2, 9·2 per cent CO, 4·3 per cent H_2, 0·4 per cent CH_4, 77·3 pe
cent N_2 by volume. The exhaust temperature was 427°C and th
room temperature 27°C. Determine the air-fuel ratio used and th
enthalpy of the dry exhaust gases and of the vapour, reckoned abov
room temperature and expressed per kg of fuel. Take mean values c
c_p from tables.   (10·84; 4740 kJ/kg; 3512 kJ/kg

5.24 The enthalpy of combustion of liquid heptane, C_7H_{16}, with liqui
water in the products is −48·074 MJ/kg at 25°C. The enthalpy o
vaporisation of C_7H_{16} at 25°C is 365 kJ/kg.

Determine the calorific value of heptane for the following condi
tions:

(a) constant pressure combustion at 25°C with C_7H_{16} vapour and
the water in the products as liquid,

(b) as (a) but with the water in the vapour state,

    (c) constant volume combustion at 25°C with the C_7H_{16} liquid and the water liquid,

    (d) as (c) but with C_7H_{16} vapour and water as vapour.

                          (48·439, 44·923, 47·975, 44.997 MJ/kg)

25 Determine the heat transfer when 0·1 kg of benzene, C_6H_6, is burned at constant pressure in 2·0 kg of air, the reactants being at 79°C and the products at 529°C. Take all the necessary data from the tables and use mean specific heats.   (−3 MJ)

26 A producer gas contains CO, H_2 and N_2 only. The producer is supplied with a mixture of air and steam and the fuel may be regarded as pure carbon. Using standard data determine the mass ratios of steam and air to fuel, the percentage volumetric analysis and the gross calorific value of the gas in MJ/m³ at 1·013 bar, 25°C.
            (0·686: 3·12:1; 41·2 per cent CO, 18·4 per cent H_2,
                          40·4 per cent N_2; 6·8 MJ/m³)

27 A mixture of methane and air at 298 K is required to produce an adiabatic flame temperature of 2000 K. Determine the percentage mixture strength required.   (86·7 per cent)

28 A four-cylinder Diesel engine develops 56 kW at 1700 rev/min. The specific fuel consumption is 0·226 kg/kWh, the fuel has an ultimate analysis of 86 per cent C, 14 per cent H_2 and a gross calorific value of 45·5 MJ/kg. The analysis of the dry exhaust gas indicates 9·8 per cent CO_2 together with some oxygen and nitrogen. The temperature of the exhaust is 327°C and the air intake temperature is 25°C. The flow rate of the engine cooling water is 32 kg/min and its temperature rises by 20 K.

    Draw up an account of the energy distribution for this engine.
             (Power 34.9 per cent, Water 27·9 per cent, Dry gas 14·9
            per cent, Vapour 8·3 per cent, unaccounted 14 per cent)

29 A small superheater is fired with 0·6 m³/min of natural gas which may be treated as pure methane, CH_4, at 25°C, 1·02 bar. The dry products of combustion contain 10 per cent by volume of CO_2 and are at a temperature of 377°C. The steam flow rate is 2000 kg/h entering at 20 bar, 0·98 dryness fraction and leaving at 20 bar, 300°C.

Determine the efficiency of the superheater and tabulate an energy balance for the unit.

(45·7 per cent; steam 45·7 per cent, dry gas 14 per cent vapour 14·4 per cent, unaccounted 25·9 per cent

5.30 A 10 per cent rich mixture of heptane, C_7H_{16}, at 18·5 bar, 405°C is burned at constant volume in a petrol engine. The products of combustion are CO_2, CO, H_2O, H_2, O_2 and N_2 only. If the maximum pressure reached is 75·8 atmospheres, find the maximum temperature and the approximate proportion of carbon burnt to carbon monoxide.

(2600 K; 24 per cent

Solutions

5.1 For 'correct' combustion with oxygen

$$C_9H_{20} + 14\,O_2 = 9\,CO_2 + 10\,H_2O$$

Air contains 79 per cent nitrogen and 21 per cent oxygen by volume giving $N_2/O_2 = 3.76$ (see page 20 of tables*).
Hence for combustion with minimum air
$$C_9H_{20} + 14\,O_2 + (14 \times 3·76)\,N_2 = 9\,CO_2 + 10\,H_2O$$
$$+ (14 \times 3·76)\,N_2$$

For nonane $M = (9 \times 12) + (20 \times 1) = 128$

$$\therefore \quad \text{Air/fuel by mass} = \frac{(14 \times 32) + (14 \times 3·76 \times 28)}{128}$$

$$= \underline{15·0 \text{ kg air/kg fuel.}}$$

Stoichiometric products

	moles	per cent vol
CO_2	9.00	12·57
H_2O	10·00	13·96
N_2	52·64	73·47
	71·64	100·00

(a)

20 per cent excess gives $15·0 \times 1·2 = \underline{18·0 \text{ kg air.}}$
Excess $O_2 = 0·2 \times 14 = 2·8$ moles.

* Ref 4

Products

	moles	per cent vol
CO_2	9·00	10·6
O_2	2·80	3·29
H_2O	10·00	11·76
N_2	63·17	74·35
	84·97	100·00

(b)

80 per cent of stoichiometric gives $0.8 \times 15.0 = \underline{12.0 \text{ kg air.}}$

Here we assume that all the hydrogen burns but that some of the carbon burns only to CO instead of CO_2

$$C_9H_{20} + (0.8 \times 14) O_2 + (0.8 \times 14 \times 3.76) N_2$$
$$= a\, CO_2 + b\, CO + 10\, H_2O + (0.8 \times 14 \times 3.76) N_2$$

Balancing carbon atoms $\quad a + b = 9 \qquad\qquad (i)$

,, $\quad$ oxygen $\quad$,, $\qquad 22.4 = 2a + b + 10$

$$\therefore \quad 2a + b = 12.4 \qquad\qquad (ii)$$

Subtracting (i) from (ii) $\quad a = 3.4 \qquad b = 5.6$

Products

	moles	per cent vol
CO_2	3·4	5·57
CO	5·6	9·17
N_2	42·112	68·89
H_2O	10·0	16·37
	61·112	100·00

(c)

5.2 The combustion equations are

$$C_4H_8 + 6 O_2 = 4 CO_2 + 4 H_2O$$
$$CH_4 + 2 O_2 = CO_2 + 2 H_2O$$
$$CO + \tfrac{1}{2} O_2 = CO_2$$
$$H_2 + \tfrac{1}{2} O_2 = H_2O$$

The following table shows the moles of oxygen required and the products—

Gas	Moles	O_2	Products CO_2	N_2
O_2	0·4	−0·4		
CO_2	4·0	0·0	4·0	
C_4H_8	2·0	12·0	8·0	
CH_4	20·0	40·0	20·0	
CO	18·0	9·0	18·0	
H_2	49·4	24·7		
N_2	6·2	0·0		6·2
	100·0	85·3	50·0	6·2

$$\text{Air/fuel} = \frac{85\cdot3}{0\cdot21 \times 100} = \underline{4\cdot06}$$

Let the air supplied be A moles/mole of gas

Dry Products	Moles
CO_2	50
N_2	6·2 + 79A
O_2	21A − 85·3

$$\therefore \quad \text{per cent } CO_2 = \frac{50 \times 100}{6\cdot2 + 100A - 85\cdot3 + 50} = \frac{50}{A - 0\cdot291}$$

$$\therefore \quad A = \frac{50}{\% \ CO_2} + 0\cdot291$$

5.3 Two alternative methods of solving the problem are given.
Method 1

Write the combustion equation for x kg air/kg fuel

$$a\left[\frac{0\cdot862C}{12} + \frac{0\cdot138H_2}{2} + \frac{0\cdot233xO_2}{32} + \frac{0\cdot767xN_2}{28}\right]$$
$$= 9\cdot8 \ CO_2 + 8\cdot1 \ O_2 + 82\cdot1 \ N_2 + b \ H_2O$$

Balancing carbon atoms $\dfrac{0.862}{12}a = 9.8$ $\therefore$ $a = 136.6$

Balancing H_2 $\dfrac{0.138}{2} \times 136.6 = b$ $\therefore$ $b = 9.43$

Balancing O_2 $\dfrac{0.233x}{32} \times 136.6 = 9.8 + 8.1 + \dfrac{9.43}{2}$

$\therefore$ $x = \underline{22.74 \text{ kg air/kg fuel}}$

Method 2

Dry exhaust	Moles n	M	Mass nM	Mass carbon
CO_2	9.8	44	$431.2 \times \dfrac{12}{44} = 117.6$	117.6
O_2	8.1	32	259.2	
N_2	82.1	28	2298.8	
	100.0		2989.2	117.6

But mass of carbon in fuel $= 0.862$ kg/kg

Mass of dry gas/kg fuel $= \dfrac{2989.2}{117.6} \times 0.862 = 21.9$

Mass of water produced $= 0.138 \times 9 = 1.242$ kg
Mass of air $= 21.91 + 1.242 - 1.0 = \underline{22.152 \text{ kg/kg fuel}}$

5.4   The combustion equation for the given case is

$$\underset{\text{(liq)}}{C_{10}H_{22}} + 15.5\,O_2 = 10\,CO_2 + \underset{\text{(liq)}}{11\,H_2O}$$

Hence 15·5 gaseous moles become 10 moles and $\Delta n = -5.5$

Now $H = U + pV$

$dH = dU + pdV + Vdp$

For isothermal constant pressure combustion

$$\Delta H = \Delta U + p\Delta V \quad \text{and} \quad p(\Delta V) = (\Delta n)R_0 T$$

$$\therefore \quad \Delta H = \Delta U + \Delta n R_0 T$$

$$\Delta U = \Delta H - \Delta n R_0 T$$

$$= -47 \cdot 45 \frac{MJ}{kg}$$

$$+ \frac{5 \cdot 5 \times 8 \cdot 3143 \times 298}{142 \times 1000} \left[\frac{kJ \ K}{kg \ mole \ K} \right] \left[\frac{kg \ mole}{kg} \frac{MJ}{kJ} \right]$$

$$= -47 \cdot 45 + 0 \cdot 096 = \underline{-47 \cdot 354 \ MJ/kg}$$

When there is vapour H_2O in the products 15·5 gaseous moles become 21 moles and $\Delta n = +5 \cdot 5$

Now h_{fg} at 25°C = 2441·8 kJ/kg

Thus the enthalpy of the products is greater by

$$\frac{11 \times 18 \times 2441 \cdot 8}{1000 \times 142} = 3 \cdot 41 \ MJ/kg$$

and $\quad \Delta H_{25} = -47 \cdot 450 + 3 \cdot 41 = -44 \cdot 04 \ MJ/kg$

$$\therefore \quad \Delta U = -44 \cdot 04 - 0 \cdot 096 = \underline{-44 \cdot 136 \ MJ/kg \ C_{10}H_{22}}$$

(Note that the change from liquid to vapour H_2O is much more significant than the difference between ΔH and ΔU.)

5.5 On page 18 of the Mayhew and Rogers tables we have the reaction

$$\underset{\text{(vap)}}{C_8H_{18}} + 12 \cdot 5 \ O_2 = 8 \ CO_2 + 9 \ \underset{\text{(vap)}}{H_2O}$$

for which ΔH at 25°C is $-5116 \cdot 1$ MJ/kg mole.

This reaction fits the data of this problem except that the products are at 473 K instead of 298 K. Hence the enthalpy of the products, H_P, is greater by $\Delta H_P = \sum n c_p (473 - 298)$.

We must not forget that the products will contain $12 \cdot 5 \times 3 \cdot 76$ moles of nitrogen since combustion is in air not pure oxygen.

$$\Delta H_P = 175[(8 \times 44 \times 0 \cdot 926) + (9 \times 1 \cdot 894 \times 18) + (12 \cdot 5 \times 3 \cdot 76$$
$$\times 1 \cdot 043 \times 28)] = 250 \ 990 \ kJ/kg \ mole \ C_8H_{18}$$

$$\Delta H = H_P - H_R = -5116 \cdot 1 + 250 \cdot 99 = -4865 \cdot 1 \ MJ/kg \ mole$$

$$Q = \Delta H = \underline{-4865 \cdot 1 \ MJ/kg \ mole \ C_8H_{18}}$$

Mean specific heats are not highly accurate and an enthalpy table should be used for greater accuracy. The method is shown below using the table of Appendix A.

$$H_{P2} - H_{P1} = \sum[n(h_2 - h_1)]$$

The table gives values in kJ/kg mole

	n	h_2	h_1	$h_2 - h_1$	$n(h_2 - h_1)$
CO_2	8	$-386\,405$	$-393\,520$	7115	56 920
H_2O	9	$-235\,882$	$-241\,830$	5948	53 532
N_2	47	$5\,109$	0	5109	240 123
					350 575

$$\therefore \quad Q = \Delta H = H_P - H_R = -5116{\cdot}1 + 350{\cdot}575$$
$$= -4765{\cdot}5 \text{ MJ/kg mole } C_8H_{18}$$

This figure is 2 per cent less than that from the calculation using mean specific heats.

5.6 The adiabatic flame temperature is the temperature reached in an adiabatic steady-flow combustion process. The energy equation for the process shows that the enthalpy of the products, H_P, is the same as that of the reactants, H_R.

$$H_P = H_R$$

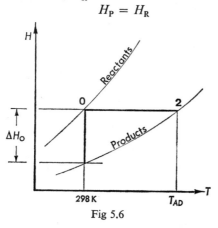

Fig 5.6

For C_6H_6 $\quad H_P - H_R$ at 298 K $= \Delta H_0 = -3169{\cdot}5$ MJ/kg mole

$$H_{P2} - H_{P0} = H_{R0} - H_{P0} = -\Delta H_0$$

$$H_{P2} - H_{P0} = 3169{\cdot}5 \text{ MJ/kg mole } C_6H_6 \qquad (i)$$

87

Assuming no dissociation

$$C_6H_6 + 1.2 \times 7.5\,O_2 + (3.76 \times 7.5 \times 1.2)N_2$$
(vap)

$$= 6\,CO_2 + 1.5\,O_2 + 3\,H_2O + 33.84\,N_2$$
(vap)

$$C_6H_6 + 9\,O_2 + 33.84\,N_2 = 6\,CO_2 + 1.5\,O_2 + 3\,H_2O + 33.84\,N_2$$
(vap)   (vap)

Equation (i) may now be solved by trial

	n moles	h_{298} MJ/mole	nh_{298} MJ	h_{2200} MJ/mole	nh_{2200} MJ	h_{2300} MJ/mole	nh_{2300} MJ
CO_2	6	−393.5	−2361.0	−289.7	−1738.2	−283.6	−1701.6
O_2	1.5	0	0	66.8	100.2	70.6	105.9
H_2O	3.0	−241.8	−725.4	−158.6	−475.8	−153.4	−460.2
N_2	33.84	0	0	63.4	2145.5	67.0	2267.3
			−3086.4		31.7		211.4
					3086.4		3086.4
				$H_{P2} - H_{P0} = 3118.1$			3297.8

Interpolating between these for 3169.5 MJ gives $T_{AD} = \underline{2229\ K}$

For greater accuracy further results could be calculated and plotted if this is justifiable.

When 20 per cent of N_2 is replaced with O_2 the products are:

	n moles	nh_{298} MJ	nh_{2200} MJ	nh_{2300} MJ
CO_2	6	−2361.0	−1738.2	−1701.6
O_2	7.42	0	495.7	523.9
H_2O	3.0	−725.4	−475.8	−460.2
N_2	27.07	0	1716.2	1813.7
		−3086.4	−2.1	175.8
			3086.4	3086.4
			3084.3	3262.2

Interpolation gives $T_{AD} = \underline{2248\ K}$.

5.7   Boiler efficiency $= \dfrac{\text{heat to steam}}{\text{energy supplied in fuel}}$

$$= \frac{\dot{m}_s(h_s - h_f)}{\dot{m}_F \times Q_{gr}}$$

where $\dot{m}_s$ = steam flow rate, h_s = steam enthalpy

$\dot{m}_F$ = fuel flow rate, Q_{gr} = gross calorific value of fuel

h_f = enthalpy of feed water

$$\eta = \frac{1500(2761 \cdot 2 - 209 \cdot 3)}{115 \times 45 \cdot 3 \times 10^3} \times 100 = \underline{73 \cdot 5 \text{ per cent}}$$

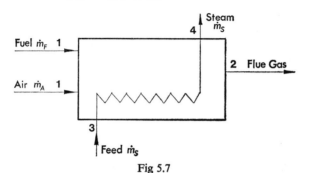

Fig 5.7

Applying the steady flow energy equation we have

$$Q - 0 = H_4 + H_2 - H_1 - H_3$$

Rearranging $\quad 0 = (H_4 - H_3) + (H_2 - H_1) + (-Q)$

Now $\quad (H_2 - H_1) = (H_{P2} - H_{R1}) = (H_{P2} - H_{P0}) + (H_{P0} - H_{R0})$
$$- (H_{R1} - H_{R0})$$

No temperature is quoted with the calorific value and we have seen that the changes in this value are small for small changes of temperature. Hence we assume that $(H_{R1} - H_{R0})$ is zero since $T_1 = T_0 = 25°C$ and that $(H_{P0} - H_{R0}) = \dot{m}_F \times \Delta H_1$

$$(H_{P2} - H_{P0}) = \sum n(h_2 - h_1)$$

where the enthalpies are given in the table of Appendix A.

(Alternatively we could again use $\sum mc_p (T_2 - T_1)$ taking mean c_p values from the tables.)

Hence the energy balance becomes

$$\dot{m}_F(-\Delta H_1) = \dot{m}_s(h_4 - h_3) + \sum_{\text{products}} n(h_2 - h_1) + (-Q)$$

$(-Q)$ is the unaccounted 'heat loss'.

Dividing through by $\dot{m}_F$ the balance is expressed per unit mass of fuel.

$$(-\Delta H_1) = \frac{\dot{m}_s}{\dot{m}_F}\underset{\text{steam}}{(h_4 - h_3)} + \underset{\text{products}}{\frac{\sum n}{\dot{m}_F}(h_2 - h_1)} + \underset{\text{losses}}{\frac{1}{\dot{m}_F}(-Q)} \qquad (i)$$
$$\text{fuel}$$

To find the number of moles of products we write the combustion equation

$$\frac{0\cdot86}{12}\,C + \frac{0\cdot14}{2}\,H_2 + 0\cdot21x\,O_2 + 0\cdot79x\,N_2 = a\,CO_2 + b\,O_2$$
$$+ d\,N_2 + f\,H_2O$$

Balancing C $\qquad\qquad a = \dfrac{0\cdot86}{12} = 0\cdot07167$

Balancing H_2 $\qquad\qquad f = 0\cdot07$

From the analysis of the products

$$\frac{a}{b} = \frac{0\cdot098}{0\cdot0742} \qquad \therefore \quad b = 0\cdot07167 \times \frac{0\cdot0742}{0\cdot098} = 0\cdot0541$$

Similarly $\qquad\qquad d = \dfrac{0\cdot07167 \times 0\cdot828}{0\cdot098} = 0\cdot6055$

Products	moles/kg fuel n'	h_2 600 K MJ/mole	h_1 298 K MJ/mole	$n'(h_2 - h_1)$ MJ
CO_2	0·07167	−380·6	−393·5	0·925
O_2	0·0541	9·238	0	0·500
N_2	0·6055	8·889	0	5·375
			dry gas total	6.800
H_2O	0·07	−231·4	−285·8	3·810

$$\frac{\dot{m}_s}{\dot{m}_F}(h_4 - h_3) = \frac{1500}{115}(2761 - 209\cdot3) = 33\,280\text{ kJ/kg fuel}$$
$$= 33\cdot28\text{ MJ/kg fuel}$$

$$(-\Delta H_1) = 45\cdot300\text{ MJ/kg fuel}$$

Using equation (i) $\quad \dfrac{(-Q)}{\dot{m}_F} = 1\cdot49\text{ MJ/kg fuel}$

Energy Balance for 1 kg fuel

Credit	MJ/kg fuel	Per cent	Debit	MJ/kg fuel	Per cent
fuel	45·300	100	To steam	33·28	73·5
			To dry flue gas	6·81	15·0
			To vapour in flue	3·81	8·4
			Losses $(-Q)$	1·40	3·1
	45·300	100		45·30	100·0

5.8 Consider a time interval of one second

$$\dot{m}_F = \frac{0·245 \times 110}{3600} = 0·0075 \text{ kg/s}$$

$$\dot{m}_F Q_{gr} = 0·0075 \times 44 \times 10^3 = 330 \text{ kW}$$

$$\text{Thermal efficiency} = \frac{110}{330} \times 100 = \underline{33·3 \text{ per cent}}$$

$$\dot{m}_{cw} c_p (T_{out} - T_{in}) = \frac{60}{60} \times 4·18 \times 24 = 100·3 \text{ kW}$$

$$\dot{Q} - \dot{W} = (H_{P2} - H_{R1}) + \Delta H_{cw}$$

assuming that the calorific value is stated for condition (1)

$$\dot{Q} - \dot{W} = (H_{P2} - H_{P1}) + \Delta H_1 - (H_{R1} - H_{R1}) + \Delta H_{cw}$$

$$= \underset{\text{products}}{\sum n(h_2 - h_1)} - \underset{\text{fuel}}{\dot{m}_F Q_{gr}} - 0 + \underset{\substack{\text{cooling} \\ \text{water}}}{\Delta H_{cw}}$$

$$\dot{m}_F Q_{gr} = \dot{W} + \sum n(h_2 - h_1) + \dot{m}_{cw} c_p (T_{out} - T_{in}) + (-\dot{Q})$$

where $(-\dot{Q})$ is the unaccounted loss.

The combustion equation for x moles air/kg fuel is:

$$\frac{0·86}{12} C + \frac{0·14}{2} H_2 + 0·21x O_2 + 0·79x N_2$$

$$= \ a \ CO_2 + b \ O_2 + d \ N_2 + f \ H_2O$$

$$\therefore \ a = 0·07167 \qquad f = 0·07$$

$$a + b + \frac{f}{2} = 0.21x \qquad b = 0.21x - 0.035 - 0.07167$$

$$= 0.21x - 0.10667$$

$$d = 0.79x$$

But the dry exhaust gas contains 8·9 per cent CO_2

$$\text{and per cent } CO_2 = \frac{a}{a + b + d} \times 100$$

$$\therefore \quad 0.089 = \frac{0.07167}{0.07167 + x - 0.10667}$$

$\therefore \quad x = 0.84$ moles of air/kg fuel

Hence $b = 0.0697$ and $d = 0.664$

Dry Products

	moles/kg fuel n	$h_2(650 \text{ K})$ kJ/mole	$h_1(298 \text{ K})$ kJ/mole	$n(h_2 - h_1)$ kJ/kg fuel
CO_2	0·07167	− 378 224	− 393 520	1096
O_2	0·06970	10 855	0	757
N_2	0·664	10 402	0	6903
				8756
H_2O	0·07	− 229 532	− 285 782	3938

Dry gas $\Delta H = 8756 \times 0.0075 = 65.67$ kW

Vapour $\Delta H = 3938 \times 0.0075 = 29.54$ kW

Energy Balance

Credit	kW	Per cent	Debit	kW	Per cent
Fuel	330	100	Useful power	110	33·3
			Cooling water	100·3	30·4
			Dry exhaust	65·67	19·9
			Exhaust vapour	29·54	8·9
			Losses	25·49	7·5
	330	100		330	100

5.9 (a) The dissociation reaction is $H_2 \rightarrow 2H$

At 3000 K $\qquad \log K = 1\cdot604^*$ $\qquad \therefore \quad K = 40\cdot179$

But $\qquad K = \dfrac{p_{H_2}}{(p_H)^2} = \dfrac{x_{H_2}}{(x_H)^2 P} = \dfrac{x_{H_2}}{(x_H)^2}\left(\dfrac{1\cdot01325}{2}\right)$

Note that the tables use p in atmospheres and 1 atm = 1·01325 bar.

Now $\quad x_{H_2} + x_H = 1$
$$\therefore \quad (x_H)^2 = \frac{(1 - x_H)}{40\cdot179}\left(\frac{1\cdot01325}{2}\right)$$

$x_H = 0\cdot1057$

$x_{H_2} = 0\cdot8943$

(b) $\qquad\qquad CO + H_2O = CO_2 + H_2$

$$K = \frac{p_{H_2O}p_{CO}}{p_{H_2}p_{CO_2}} = \frac{x_{H_2O}x_{CO}}{x_{H_2}x_{CO_2}} = \frac{0\cdot554 \times 0\cdot1}{0\cdot1 \times 0\cdot246} = 2\cdot25$$
$$\log K = \log 2\cdot25 = 0\cdot352$$

$\therefore \quad$ temperature is approximately 1400 K

5.10 The stoichiometric equation is
$$C_8H_{18} + 12\cdot5\,O_2 = 8\,CO_2 + 9\,H_2O$$

The mixture used is 20 per cent rich

$\therefore \quad \dfrac{12\cdot5}{1\cdot2}$ moles O_2 are supplied together with $\dfrac{12\cdot5}{1\cdot2} \times 3\cdot76$ moles N_2

that is 10·417 moles O_2 and 39·167 moles N_2

The equation is
$$C_8H_{18} + 10\cdot417\,O_2 + 39\cdot167\,N_2 = a\,CO_2 + b\,CO$$
$$+ d\,H_2O + e\,H_2 + f\,O_2 + 39\cdot167\,N_2$$

The dissociation constants at 2700 K are

$$K_1 = \frac{p_{H_2O}p_{CO}}{p_{H_2}p_{CO_2}} = \frac{db}{ea} \qquad \log K_1 = 0\cdot8155 \qquad K_1 = 6\cdot5388$$

$$K_2 = \frac{p_{CO_2}}{p_{CO}p_{O_2}^{\frac{1}{2}}} = \frac{a}{b}\left[\frac{\sum n_P}{fp}\right]^{\frac{1}{2}} \qquad \log K_2 = 1\cdot005 \qquad K_2 = 10\cdot116$$

---

* The dissociation constants used in this chapter are based on Ref 4 1st edition 1964 which differ from those of the 1967 edition.

The pressure p is in atmospheres and although the combustion is at constant volume the number of moles is changing.

$$p = \frac{18\cdot4 \times 2700}{1\cdot01325 \times 680} \times \frac{\sum n_P}{50\cdot584} \text{ atmospheres}$$

Balancing   C $(a + b) = 8$ (i)

  ,, O_2 $a + \frac{1}{2}b + \frac{1}{2}d + f = 10\cdot417$ (ii)

  ,, H_2 $d + e = 9$ (iii)

and from the dissociation

$$\frac{db}{ea} = 6\cdot5388 \tag{iv}$$

and $$f = \left(\frac{a}{b}\right)^2 \times \frac{1\cdot01325 \times 680 \times 50\cdot584}{10\cdot116^2 \times 18\cdot4 \times 2700}$$

$$\therefore \quad f = 6\cdot8557 \times 10^{-3}\left(\frac{a}{b}\right)^2 \tag{v}$$

We have to show that per cent C burned to CO $= \dfrac{b}{8} = 0\cdot415$ that is $b = 3\cdot32$

Hence from   (i) $a = 4\cdot68$

   from   (v) $f = 0\cdot0136$

   from   (iii) and (iv) $d = 8\cdot12$

Substituting these values in (ii) the left hand side becomes $10\cdot4136$ which shows good agreement with equation (ii).

Using the enthalpy data of Appendix A and taking the enthalpy of C_8H_{18} at 25°C as $-208\cdot5$ MJ/kg mole the student may check that these results are consistent with the energy balance for the reaction allowing for some heat transfer to the surroundings. (Conversion to internal energies will be required.)

6

Two-phase Working Fluids

Questions

1. Sketch p–v, p–h and T–s diagrams for (a) CO_2 (b) H_2O.

2. If the pressure of a vapour is increased at constant temperature, what will happen?

3. Under what circumstances is it reasonable to treat steam as an ideal gas?

4. Explain what is meant by the Rankine Cycle. How does it differ from the Carnot Cycle for a vapour?

5. Under what conditions will the feed pump term be significant in a Rankine Cycle efficiency calculation?

6. Explain the operation of regenerative feed heating.

7. Describe a reheat steam power cycle and suggest two reasons for its use.

8. Sketch a p–h diagram for a simple vapour compression refrigerator.

9. If the pressure difference between condensation and evaporation is increased in a vapour compression refrigerator, what will happen to the coefficient of performance?

10. What is a binary vapour cycle?

Worked Problems

6.1 A steam power cycle is to operate with a boiler pressure of 50 bar and a condenser pressure of 0·07 bar. The steam leaving the boiler is at a temperature of 350°C. Compare the efficiency, specific steam

consumption and work ratio of the Rankine Cycle with correspondi
values for a Carnot Cycle working with saturated steam betwee
the same temperature limits.

Calculate the new efficiency in each case when an isentrop
efficiency of 0·8 applies to all expansions and compressions.

6.2 Steam is supplied to a simple impulse turbine at 10 bar, 250°C, t
pressure in the wheel case being 1·2 bar and the nozzle efficiency
per cent. The expansion to the nozzle throat may be assumed to
isentropic for which $n = 1·3$, so that all the loss occurs in the dive
gent portion. Determine the throat and exit areas required for
steam flow rate of 10 000 kg/h.

The nozzles are inclined to the plane of rotation at 20°. The blade
are equiangular and have a velocity coefficient of 0·78. Assumir
that the ratio of the mean blade speed to steam speed at nozzle ex
is that for maximum efficiency, calculate the blade speed, the blac
angles, the power developed, the blading efficiency and the axi
thrust.

6.3 At entry to a stage in a 50 per cent reaction turbine the steam has
pressure of 3·5 bar, a dryness of 0·98 and flows at the rate of 50 kg/
The turbine speed is 1500 rev/min and the blades have a mean di
meter of 1 m. The blade inlet and exit angles are 70° and 20° respe
tively. Calculate the blade length, the power developed and the stag
pressure drop if the isentropic efficiency is 82 per cent.

6.4 The pressure at entry to a stage of a pressure compound impuls
turbine is 130 bar and the steam is superheated to 400°C. The pressure
in the wheel chamber of this stage and the next two stages are 60, 2
and 10 bar. Each stage has an isentropic efficiency of 0·78. Determin
the power developed by the three stages per kg of steam, the rehea
factor, the overall isentropic efficiency and the final steam conditio

6.5 A turbine is supplied with steam at 250 bar, 500°C which expand
in the high pressure section to 50 bar. The steam is then reheated t
500°C and expands in the low pressure section of the turbine t
0·07 bar. Determine the efficiency of this cycle not allowing for an
feed heating. Assume that the isentropic efficiency of each section c
the turbine is 0·8. Compare the result with the efficiency of th
corresponding simple Rankine cycle.

6 Steam is supplied to a turbine at a pressure of 70 bar and a temperature of 400°C and exhaust is at 0·08 bar. Some steam is bled for feed heating at 14 bar and at 2 bar. Tubular feed heaters are used in which the feed temperature may be assumed to be raised to the saturation temperature of the bled steam, the condensate (drain) leaving at the same temperature as that at which the feed water enters. This drain from the higher pressure heater is passed through the lower pressure heater from which the combined drains pass to the condenser. Calculate the mass of steam bled for each heater and the improvement in cycle efficiency compared with a cycle without feed heating. Use an isentropic efficiency of 0·78 for each portion of the expansion in both cycles.

7 A steam power cycle is to be 'topped' with a mercury cycle.
   Calculate the cycle efficiency from the following specification:

mercury boiler pressure	5 bar
temperature of mercury generated at this pressure	500°C
isentropic efficiency of adiabatic mercury turbine	75 per cent
mercury condenser pressure	0·08 bar
condensation of mercury generates steam at 30 bar,	240°C
isentropic efficiency of adiabatic steam turbine	79 per cent
steam condenser pressure	0·14 bar

Assume simple cycles with no feed heating and neglect all losses.

8 A vapour compression refrigeration system uses dichlorodifluoromethane (CF_2Cl_2) and operates between pressure limits of 7·449 and 1·509 bar. The vapour entering the compressor has a temperature of -10°C and the liquid leaving the condenser is at 28°C. A refrigerating effect of 2 kW is required. Determine the coefficient of performance and the swept volume of the compressor if it has a volumetric efficiency of 76 per cent based on intake conditions and runs at 600 rev/min.

9 Two stages of compression and expansion are used in a refrigerator in which ammonia is the refrigerant. The evaporator pressure is 1·196 bar, the condenser pressure 12·37 bar and the intermediate pressure 3·983 bar. The ammonia enters the low pressure compressor with a dryness fraction of 0·99 and leaves the condenser at 30°C. After the first expansion valve the vapour is separated and passed to the suction of the high pressure compressor. Determine (a) the mass of refrigerant passing through the condenser per minute when the refrigerating effect is 5 kW and (b) the coefficient of per formance of the plant. Neglect all losses.

6.10 The heat exchangers of a nuclear power plant deliver steam at two pressures. The high pressure flow rate is 0.97×10^6 kg/h at 45 bar 400°C and the low pressure flow rate 0.33×10^6 kg/h at 20 bar 400°C. The H.P. steam expands in a turbine having an isentropic efficiency of 0.76 to 20 bar when the two streams mix and enter the L.P. turbine. This turbine has an isentropic efficiency of 0.78 and exhausts to condenser at 0.035 bar, the condensate returning to the heat exchanger. Determine the power generated and the efficiency of the cycle.

Unworked Problems

6.11 Make sketches on T–s and h–s axes showing the ideal Rankine cycle and deduce an expression for the cycle efficiency including the effect of the feed pump.

An adiabatic turbine is supplied with steam at a pressure of 150 bar, a temperature of 700°C and exhaust is at a pressure of 0.1 bar. The expansion has an isentropic efficiency of 85 per cent. Calculate the specific steam consumption if the feed pump process is isentropic
(2.62 kg/kWh)

6.12 Deduce an expression for the efficiency of a Rankine cycle allowing for the work done by the feed pump.

A power plant uses mercury which is supplied to the turbine at 14 bar with 83 K superheat. The condenser pressure is 0.03 bar. Calculate the efficiency and specific mercury consumption for the corresponding Rankine cycle.   (39.7 per cent; 26.5 kg/kWh)

6.13 A two-row velocity compound impulse turbine stage receives steam at 160 bar, 600°C. The pressure in the wheel chamber is 80 bar, the nozzle efficiency 0.9, the nozzle angle 18° to the wheel plane and the mean blade speed is 183 m/s. If the first and second rows of moving blades have exit angles of 25° and 40° respectively and the fixed guide blades have exit angles of 18° to the wheel plane, sketch the velocity diagrams and calculate the power developed for a steam flow rate of 1 kg/s. Assume that the fluid flows into all blades without shock and neglect blade friction.   (204 kW

14 An impulse steam turbine has nozzles inclined at 20° to the plane of rotation. The inlet and exit angles of the moving blades are equal, the blade velocity coefficient is 0·8 and the mean diameter of the blades is 0·5 m. The steam leaves the nozzles at 750 m/s. Determine the optimum value of the blade angles, the steam flow rate to produce 20 kW and the diagram efficiency. The optimum condition should be deduced.   (36°–3′; 0·0895 kg/s; 79·5 per cent)

15 The blades of an impulse-reaction steam turbine have entry and exit angles of 75° and 20° respectively at a mean diameter of 0·75 m, fixed and moving blades being identical. Estimate the stage pressure drop when the speed is 2500 rev/min and the steam enters the stage at 3·5 bar, dry saturated. Isentropic expansion may be assumed.

If the tip diameter is 0·9 m and the degree of reaction, change of whirl velocity and the axial velocity are constant, find the blade angles at the tip.   (0·224 bar, 88·9°, 18·5°)

16 One stage of a 50 per cent reaction steam turbine is to receive steam at 7 bar, 200°C which will expand with an isentropic efficiency of 85 per cent to 5·5 bar. The steam flow rate is 2×10^5 kg/h and allowance should be made for a tip leakage of 5 per cent. The shaft speed will be 3000 rev/min and the mean diameter of the blades 1 m.

It is suggested that blades having entry and exit angles of 54° and 20° will be suitable. Check this, correct the angles if necessary and calculate the blade length and the power developed.
          (20°; 52·6°; 2375 kW; 0·08 m)

17 Steam having a dryness fraction of 0·96 at a pressure of 2 bar is compressed in a three stage turbo-compressor to 16 bar the overall isentropic efficiency of compression being 73 per cent. The intermediate pressures are 4 and 8 bar and the condition line may be assumed to be straight. Determine the power input required for a flow of 3000 kg/h, the reheat factor and the isentropic efficiency of each stage.   (50 kW; 1·04; 80 per cent; 76 per cent; 74 per cent)

18 Three stages of a pressure compound impulse steam turbine are to expand steam from 200 bar, 600°C to 100 bar. Each stage is to have an isentropic efficiency of 83 per cent and develop one third of the power. Use the h–s chart to estimate the intermediate pressures and the reheat factor. Calculate the power output in MW for a flow of 10^6 kg/h.

Will the second stage nozzles need to be convergent-divergent?
Find the minimum aggregate cross-sectional area of these nozzles
assuming 100 per cent isentropic efficiency. The critical pressure
ratio for superheated steam is 0·546.

(160 bar; 128 bar; 52·5 MW; 0·0194 m²)

6.19 Give reasons for the use of reheat cycles for steam turbine power
plant.

Steam is supplied to a turbine at 140 bar, 600°C and expands to
14 bar at which pressure it is reheated to 500°C and expands to a
condenser pressure of 0·05 bar. Each portion of the expansion has
an isentropic efficiency of 0·8.

Assuming a closed cycle and neglecting feed heating, determine
the cycle efficiency and the specific steam consumption in kg/MWh
when the alternator efficiency is 90 per cent.

(37·8 per cent; 2740 kg/MWh)

6.20 Blade erosion is a major problem at the low pressure end of steam
turbines; explain why and discuss possible control methods.

A turbine receives steam at 100 bar, 550°C and exhausts at 0·07
bar. A single stage of reheating is employed to 450°C at 12 bar.
Determine the cycle efficiency if the isentropic efficiency of each
section of the turbine is 82 per cent. (36·2 per cent)

6.21 Explain the thermodynamic advantages that arise from bled steam
feed heating in steam turbine circuits.

A turbine is to be supplied with steam at a pressure of 40 bar and a
temperature of 350°C. Steam will be bled for feed heating at two
points in the expansion, the higher pressure tapping being at 10 bar.
The enthalpy of the feed water is to rise by equal amounts in each
heater, the final temperature being 179·9°C. Condensation occurs at
0·07 bar.

Sketch several alternative feed heating circuits and discuss their
relative advantages. Select one circuit and by making reasonable
simplifying assumptions calculate its efficiency. The turbine isentropic
efficiency may be taken as 0·83 for each section of the expansion.

Examine the entropy production of the higher pressure heater and
suggest how it might be reduced. (33·4 per cent)

6.22 A turbine receives steam at 40 bar, 300°C and exhausts at 0·1 bar.
Two stages of indirect feed heating are employed at 3·5 bar and 0·7

bar. The condensate from the high pressure heater is passed to the low pressure heater from which the combined condensate flows to the condenser. The isentropic efficiency of each section of the turbine is 0·8.

Sketch the circuit and calculate the cycle efficiency stating any assumptions made. (30·7 per cent)

6.23 Explain the objects, advantages and limitations of regenerative feed heating as used in steam turbine plant.

Steam at 85 bar, 540°C is expanded in three turbine cylinders each of efficiency ratio 0·8 to a pressure of 0·07 bar. Steam is bled for feed heating between the cylinders at 20 bar and 2·5 bar and from each heater the condensate is pumped forward into the feed line. If the ongoing feed temperature is raised to the saturation temperature of the bled steam, estimate the mass of steam bled at each point and the cycle efficiency. (0·143 kg; 0·122 kg; 38 per cent)

6.24 In a study for a space project it is thought that condensation of a working fluid might be possible at −40°C. A binary cycle is proposed using Refrigerant 12 as the low temperature fluid and water as the high temperature fluid. Steam is generated at 80 bar, 500°C and expands in a turbine of isentropic efficiency 81 per cent to 0·05 bar at which pressure it is condensed by the generation of dry saturated Refrigerant 12 vapour at 30°C from saturated liquid at −40°C. The isentropic efficiency of the Refrigerant 12 turbine is 83 per cent. Determine the mass ratio of Refrigerant 12 to water and the efficiency of the cycle. Neglect all losses. (10·86; 44·4 per cent)

6.25 A vapour compression refrigerator is to operate condensing at 25°C, the liquid leaving the condenser being at 23°C and evaporating at −15°C. At compressor suction there is 15 K superheat. Compare the compressor capacity and the performance of two plants having the same refrigerating effect, one using Refrigerant 12 and the other ammonia.

(R12: NH₃ 1·58; Coefficients 5·52 R12, 5·36 NH₃)

6.26 A refrigeration plant evaporates Refrigerant 12 at −15°C and condenses at 30°C. The fluid leaves the evaporator at 0°C and the condenser at 28°C. It is throttled to 10°C when the separated vapour is passed to the compressor and the remaining liquid is then throttled to −15°C. Specific heat of liquid is 0·9 kJ/kg K.

Estimate the theoretical coefficient of performance and show the cycles on sketches of the T–s and p–h charts. (5·17)

6.27 A refrigerator using Refrigerant 12 is required to evaporate at $-45°C$. Two stages of compression and expansion are proposed with approximately equal pressure ratios. Condensation is to be at $25°C$ and the low pressure fluid entering the first stage compressor is at $-30°C$. The liquid entering the first throttle valve is at $20°C$. Sketch the circuit and the p–h diagram and calculate the coefficient of performance of the theoretical cycle. (2·86)

6.28 The state of Refrigerant 12 entering a compressor is $-5°C$, 1·237 bar. Isentropic compression takes place to 7·449 bar. The liquid leaving the condenser at $28°C$, 7·449 bar, passes through a heat exchanger where it is cooled by the fluid leaving the evaporator, the pressure dropping to 7·2 bar. The liquid leaving the heat exchanger is throttled to 1·509 bar and evaporated at this pressure, re-entering the heat exchanger at 1·509 bar, $-18°C$. After the heat exchanger the vapour enters the compressor at the condition specified.

Calculate the coefficient of performance of this plant. (3·63)

6.29 Steam is supplied to a pass-out turbine at 35 bar, $350°C$ and dry saturated process steam is required at 3·5 bar. The low pressure stage exhausts at 0·07 bar and the condition line may be assumed to be straight.

If the power required is 1 MW and the maximum process load is 1·4 MW, estimate the maximum steam flow through the high and low pressure stages. Assume that the steam just condenses in the process plant. (1·543 and 1·182 kg/s)

6.30 Steam is generated at 70 bar, $500°C$ and expands in a turbine to 30 bar with an isentropic efficiency of 77 per cent. At this condition it is mixed with twice its mass of steam at 30 bar, $400°C$. The mixture then expands with an isentropic efficiency of 80 per cent to 0·06 bar. At a point in the expansion where the pressure is 5 bar, steam is bled for feed heating in a direct contact heater, which raises the feed to the saturation temperature of the bled steam.

Calculate the mass of steam bled per kg of high pressure steam and the cycle efficiency. Assume that the L.P. expansion condition line is straight. (0·531 kg; 31·9 per cent)

Solutions

6.1

The Rankine Cycle

This cycle is shown as 1 2 3 4 5 on the T–s diagram, fig. 6.1.
The work output is $(h_4 - h_5)$.
The work input to the feed pump is $(h_2 - h_1)$.
But $Tds = dh - vdp$ and for an isentropic feed pump operation $ds = 0$ and v is sensibly constant.

$$\therefore \quad (h_2 - h_1) = v(p_2 - p_1)$$

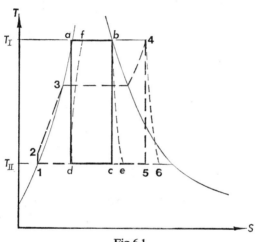

Fig 6.1

The net useful work is then $W = (h_4 - h_5) - v(p_2 - p_1)$.
The heat transfer required is $(h_4 - h_2)$.

$$\therefore \quad Q = h_4 - h_1 - v(p_2 - p_1)$$

Thus the ideal Rankine cycle efficiency is

$$\eta_R = \frac{h_4 - h_5 - v(p_2 - p_1)}{h_4 - h_1 - v(p_2 - p_1)}$$

$$= \frac{1070 - 0 \cdot 1 \times 10^{-2} \times 49 \cdot 03 \times 10^2}{3070 - 163 - 4 \cdot 903}$$

$$= 0 \cdot 367 \quad \text{or} \quad \underline{36 \cdot 7 \text{ per cent}}$$

$$\text{Specific steam consumption} = 3600 \, \frac{\text{kJ}}{\text{kWh}} \times \frac{1}{W} \, \frac{\text{kg}}{\text{kJ}}$$

$$= \frac{3600}{1065} = 3\cdot38 \, \text{kg/kWh}$$

$$\text{Work ratio} = \frac{\text{net positive work}}{\text{gross positive work}} = \frac{1065}{1070} = \underline{0\cdot995}$$

The effect of an isentropic efficiency of $0\cdot8$ will be to decrease the work of expansion and increase the feed pump work.

$$W = 1070 \times 0\cdot8 - \frac{4\cdot903}{0\cdot8} = 849\cdot9 \, \frac{\text{kJ}}{\text{kg}}$$

$$Q = 3070 - 163 - 6\cdot1 = 2900\cdot9 \, \text{kJ/kg}$$

$$\eta = 0\cdot293 \quad \text{or} \quad \underline{29\cdot3 \text{ per cent}}$$

Carnot Cycle

The efficiency in this case can be calculated from

$$\eta_C = \frac{T_I - T_{II}}{T_I}$$

Where the cycle is a b c d in fig. 6.1

$$\eta_C = \frac{623 - 312}{623} = 0\cdot499 \quad \text{or} \quad 49\cdot9 \text{ per cent}$$

This value can also be found from enthalpy values which will be required for the other quantities concerned.

Point c of fig. 6.1 will be found to be off the normal h–s chart and the tables must be used.

Putting $s_c = s_b$ gives $x_c = 0\cdot603$

$$h_c = 163 + 0\cdot603 \times 2409 = 1618 \, \text{kJ/kg}$$

Similarly $\quad x_d = 0\cdot417 \qquad h_d = 1168 \, \text{kJ/kg}$

$$\therefore \quad \eta_C = \frac{(h_b - h_c) - (h_a - h_d)}{h_b - h_a}$$

$$= \frac{(2565 - 1618) - (1670 - 1168)}{2565 - 1670} = \frac{445}{895}$$

$$= 0\cdot497 \quad \text{or} \quad \underline{49\cdot7 \text{ per cent}}$$

$$\text{Specific consumption} = \frac{3600}{445} = \underline{8\cdot1 \text{ kg/kWh}}$$

$$\text{Work ratio} = \frac{445}{947} = 0\cdot47$$

Introducing $\eta_s = 0\cdot8$ on both compression and expansion gives cycle d f b e fig. 6.1

$$\eta = \frac{0\cdot8(h_b - h_c) - \dfrac{1}{0\cdot8}(h_a - h_d)}{(h_b - h_f)} = \underline{16\cdot9 \text{ per cent}}$$

The very much greater effect of irreversibility on the Carnot cycle with its low work ratio should be noted.

6.2

The pressure at the throat of the nozzle will be given by the critical pressure ratio

$$\frac{p_t}{p_1} = \left[\frac{2}{n+1}\right]^{\frac{n}{n-1}}$$

where n is the isentropic index.

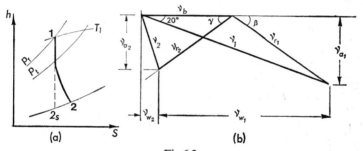

Fig 6.2

When $n = 1\cdot3$ $\quad p_t = 0\cdot546\,p_1 = 5\cdot46$ bar.

$$v_1 = 0\cdot2328 \text{ m}^3/\text{kg}$$

$$v_t = 0\cdot2328 \times \left[\frac{1}{0\cdot546}\right]^{\frac{1}{1\cdot3}} = 0\cdot37 \text{ m}^3/\text{kg}$$

$$v_t = (np_tv_t)^{\frac{1}{2}} = (1\cdot3 \times 546 \times 10^3 \times 0\cdot37)^{\frac{1}{2}} = 512 \text{ m/s}$$

$$A_t = \frac{\dot{m}v_t}{v_t} = \frac{10\,000}{3600} \times \frac{0\cdot37}{512} = \underline{0\cdot002 \text{ m}^2}$$

Plotting on the h–s chart

$$(h_1 - h_{2s}) = 404 \text{ kJ/kg}$$
$$(h_1 - h_2) = 0.91 \times 404 = 367.6 \text{ kJ/kg}$$

Using the steady flow energy equation with negligible change of potential energy and assuming that the nozzle is adiabatic with inlet velocity small compared with the exit velocity,

$$v_2 = \sqrt{(2(h_1 - h_2))} = \sqrt{(2 \times 10^3 \times 367.6)} = 858 \text{ m/s}$$
$$v_2 = x_2 v_{g_2} = 0.95 \times 1.428 = 1.357 \text{ m}^3/\text{kg}$$

where x_2 is obtained from the h–s chart.

$$\therefore \quad A_2 = \frac{10\,000}{3600} \times \frac{1.357}{858} = \underline{0.0044 \text{ m}^2}$$

Blade speed $= 858 \times \dfrac{\cos 20}{2}$ for optimum conditions.

$$= 858 \times \frac{0.9397}{2} = \underline{402 \text{ m/s}}$$

$$v_{a1} = 858 \sin 20 = 294 \text{ m/s}$$
$$v_{w1} = 2 \times 402 = 804 \text{ m/s}$$
$$\beta = \tan^{-1} \frac{294}{402} = \underline{36.1°} = \gamma \quad \text{Blade angles.}$$

$$v_{r1} = \frac{402}{\cos 36.1} = 497 \text{ m/s}$$
$$v_{r2} = 497 \times 0.78 = 388 \text{ m/s}$$
$$v_{a2} = 388 \sin \gamma = 228.2 \text{ m/s} \quad v_{r2} \cos \gamma = 314 \text{ m/s}$$
$$v_{w2} = 402 - 314 = 88 \text{ m/s}$$

$$\text{Power} = \dot{m} v_b \Delta v_w = \frac{10\,000}{3600} \frac{(804 - 88)402}{10^3} = \underline{800 \text{ kW}}$$

$$\text{Blading efficiency} = \frac{\text{Work}}{\text{Nozzle KE}} = \frac{2 v_b \Delta v_w}{v_1^2}$$

$$= \frac{2 \times 402 \times 716}{858^2} = 0.782 \quad \text{or} \quad \underline{78.2 \text{ per cent}}$$

$$\text{Axial thrust} = m \Delta v_a = \frac{10\,000}{3600}(294 - 228.2)10^{-3} = \underline{0.183 \text{ kN}}$$

6.3

Mean blade speed, $v_b = \dfrac{1500}{60} \times 2\pi \times \dfrac{1}{2} = 78.5$ m/s

$$v_1 = \sin 110 \times \frac{v_b}{\sin 50} = 96.3 \text{ m/s}$$

$$\Delta v_w = 2v_1 \cos 20 - v_b = 102.5 \text{ m/s}$$

$$v_a = v_1 \sin 20 = 32.9 \text{ m/s}$$

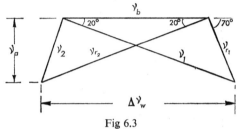

Fig 6.3

Blade annulus area $= \pi dL$ where $d =$ mean diameter and $L =$ blade length.

For axial flow through the annulus the continuity equation gives

$$\dot{m}v = v_a \pi dL$$

$$\therefore \quad L = \frac{50 \times 0.98 \times 0.5241}{32.9 \times \pi \times 1} = \underline{0.248 \text{ m}}$$

$$\text{Power} = \dot{m}v_b \Delta v_w = \frac{50 \times 78.5 \times 102.5}{10^3} = \underline{402 \text{ kW}}$$

For the isentropic expansion $dh_s = v\,dp$

$$\therefore \quad \Delta p = \frac{\Delta h_s}{v} \text{ if the pressure change is small and } v \text{ sensibly constant.}$$

$$\Delta h = \frac{-402}{50} = -8.04 \text{ kJ/kg} \qquad \Delta h_s = \frac{-8.04}{0.82} = -9.8 \text{ kJ/kg}$$

$$\therefore \quad \Delta p = \frac{-9.8}{0.98 \times 0.5241} = -19.1 \text{ kN/m}^2 = \underline{-0.191 \text{ bar}}$$

6.4

For each stage $\Delta h = 0 \cdot 78 \Delta h_s$

Plotting on the h–s chart we have

$$\Delta h_{s1} = -180 \text{ kJ/kg} \qquad \Delta h_1 = -140 \cdot 5 \text{ kJ/kg}$$

$$\Delta h_{s2} = -180 \text{ kJ/kg} \qquad \Delta h_2 = -140 \cdot 5 \text{ kJ/kg}$$

$$\Delta h_{s3} = -165 \text{ kJ/kg} \qquad \Delta h_3 = -129 \cdot 0 \text{ kJ/kg}$$

$$\Delta h_{so} = -515 \text{ kJ/kg}$$

$$\sum \Delta h_s = -525 \text{ kJ/kg}$$

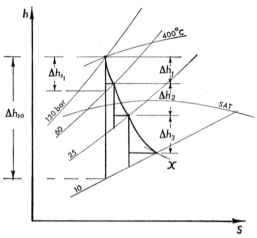

Fig 6.4

The reheat factor $= \dfrac{\sum \Delta h_s}{\Delta h_{so}} = \dfrac{525}{515} = \underline{1 \cdot 02}$

The power developed $= -\sum \Delta h = \underline{410 \text{ kJ/kg}}$

The final dryness $x = \underline{0 \cdot 92}$

The overall isentropic efficiency $= \dfrac{410}{515} = \underline{0 \cdot 796}$

6.5

Using the h–s diagram $\qquad h_1 = 3165 \text{ kJ/kg}$

Note that this is a supercritical condition and the enthalpy could be obtained from page 9 of the Mayhew and Rogers tables.*

* Ref 4

$$h_{2s} = 2780 \text{ kJ/kg}$$

$$\Delta h_s = -385 \text{ kJ/kg} \qquad \Delta h_H = 0.8 \Delta h_s = -308 \text{ kJ/kg}$$

$$h_2 = 2857 \text{ kJ/kg}$$

$$h_3 = 3433 \text{ kJ/kg} \qquad h_{4s} = 2165 \text{ kJ/kg}$$

$$\Delta h_s = -1268 \text{ kJ/kg} \qquad \Delta h_L = 0.8 \Delta h_s = -1014 \text{ kJ/kg}$$

$$\text{Work transfer} = -(\Delta h_H + \Delta h_L) = 1322 \text{ kJ/kg}$$

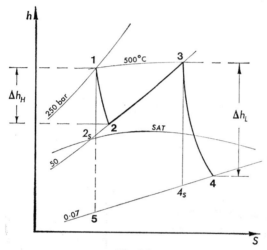

Fig 6.5

Assuming that the feed returns at the saturation temperature corresponding to 0·07 bar, the heat transfer required to raise steam at state (1) is $3165 - 163 = 3002 \text{ kJ/kg}$

Reheat required $= h_3 - h_2 = 576 \text{ kJ/kg}$

$$\text{Cycle efficiency} = \left(\frac{1322}{3002 + 576}\right) \times 100 = \underline{36 \cdot 9 \text{ per cent}}$$

Point (5) is at the end of the straight Rankine cycle expansion and is off the range of the printed h–s chart.

$$s_1 = 5 \cdot 962 \text{ kJ/kg K} \qquad \text{and} \qquad s_5 = s_1$$

$$\therefore \quad 5 \cdot 962 = 0 \cdot 559 + x_5 \times 7 \cdot 715$$

$$x_5 = 0 \cdot 7$$

(Note that this would be intolerably wet for a practical cycle.)

$$\therefore \quad h_5 = 163 + 0{\cdot}7 \times 2409 = 1849 \text{ kJ/kg}$$

Rankine cycle efficiency $= \dfrac{3165 - 1849}{3165 - 163} = 0{\cdot}438 \quad \text{or} \quad \underline{43{\cdot}8 \text{ per cent}}$

If the straight cycle had an isentropic efficiency of $0{\cdot}8$ the cycle efficiency would be 35 per cent. We see that the reheat causes an improvement in efficiency in addition to raising the turbine exhaust dryness fraction.

6.6

$\eta_s = \dfrac{\Delta h}{\Delta h_s} = 0.78$ for each portion of the expansion. Using this, the

h–s diagram may be plotted on the printed chart and values tabulated in kJ/kg.

h_o	h_1	$(h_o - h_1)$	h_2	$(h_1 - h_2)$	h_3	$(h_2 - h_3)$
3158	2862	296	2585	277	2231	354

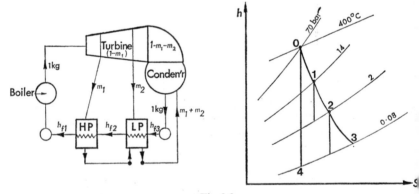

Fig 6.6

Consider the control volume formed by the casing of the high pressure heater and apply the steady flow energy equation,

$$0 = 1\,h_{f1} + m_1 h_{f2} - 1\,h_{f2} - m_1 h_1$$

$$\therefore \quad m_1 = \frac{h_{f1} - h_{f2}}{h_1 - h_{f2}} = \frac{830 - 505}{2862 - 505} = 0{\cdot}138 \text{ kg}$$

Applying the energy equation to the low pressure heater gives

$$0 = 1 h_{f2} + (m_1 + m_2) h_{f3} - 1 h_{f3} - m_2 h_2 - m_1 h_{f2}$$

whence
$$m_2 = \underline{0\cdot118 \text{ kg}}$$

Work transfer $= 1(h_0 - h_1) + (1 - m_1)(h_1 - h_2)$
$$+ (1 - m_1 - m_2)(h_2 - h_3)$$
$$= 296 + 0\cdot862 \times 277 + 0\cdot744 \times 354 = 798 \text{ kJ}$$

Cycle efficiency $= \dfrac{798}{h_0 - h_{f1}} = \dfrac{798}{2328} = 0\cdot342$ or $\underline{34\cdot2 \text{ per cent}}$

With no feed heating, $h_0 - h_4 = 1142 \text{ kJ/kg}$

$$\eta = \frac{1142 \times 0\cdot78}{3158 - 174} = \underline{29\cdot9 \text{ per cent}}$$

There is an improvement by $4\cdot3$ per cent when feed heating is employed.

7

Mercury

$$s_1 = s_g + c_p \ln \frac{T_1}{T_{sat}}$$

$$s_1 = 0\cdot5294 + 0\cdot1036 \ln \frac{773}{733\cdot7} = 0\cdot53478 \text{ kJ/kg K}$$

$$s_{2s} = s_1 = 0\cdot0870 + x_{2s} \times 0\cdot5721 = 0\cdot53478$$

Whence
$$x_{2s} = 0\cdot783$$

$$h_{2s} = 33\cdot21 + (0\cdot783 \times 294\cdot7) = 264\cdot21 \text{ kJ/kg}$$

$$h_1 = h_g + c_p(T_1 - T_{sat}) = 352\cdot78 + 0\cdot1036 \times 39\cdot3$$
$$= 356\cdot95 \text{ kJ/kg}$$

$$\Delta h_s = -92\cdot74 \text{ kJ/kg}$$

$$\Delta h = -92\cdot74 \times 0\cdot75 = -69\cdot56 \text{ kJ/kg}$$

$$h_2 = h_1 + \Delta h = 356\cdot95 - 69\cdot56 = 287\cdot39 \text{ kJ/kg}$$

$$h_3 = 33\cdot21 \text{ kJ/kg}$$

Heat transfer to water during condensation of mercury

$$= h_2 - h_3 = 254 \cdot 18 \text{ kJ/kg}$$

Heat transfer required to raise 1 kg steam $= h_5 - h_4$

$$= 2825 - 220 = 2605 \text{ kJ/kg}$$

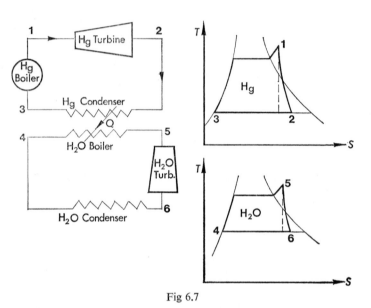

Fig 6.7

Hence mercury required $= \dfrac{2605}{254 \cdot 18} = 10 \cdot 25 \text{ kg/kg } H_2O$

Steam Turbine work $= (h_5 - h_6) = 0 \cdot 79(h_5 - h_{6s})$

$$= 0 \cdot 79(2825 - 2005) = 648 \text{ KJ/kg}$$

Total work $= 648 + 10 \cdot 25 \times 69 \cdot 56 = 1360 \text{ kJ/kg } H_2O$

Heat transfer required by mercury

$$= m(h_1 - h_3) = 10 \cdot 25(356 \cdot 95 - 33 \cdot 21) = 3315 \text{ kJ}$$

Cycle efficiency $= \dfrac{1360}{3315} = 0 \cdot 41$ or   <u>41 per cent</u>

6.8

The condition at (1) is superheated by 10 K. Interpolating between saturation and 15 K superheated gives $h_1 = 184.74$ kJ/kg

$$s_1 = 0.7317 \text{ kJ/kg K}$$

$$s_2 = s_1$$

$$\therefore \quad h_2 = 210.63 + \frac{(221.44 - 210.63)(0.7317 - 0.7208)}{(0.7540 - 0.7208)}$$

$$= 214.18 \text{ kJ/kg}$$

$h_3 = 62.64$ kJ/kg for liquid at 28°C

$h_4 = h_3$

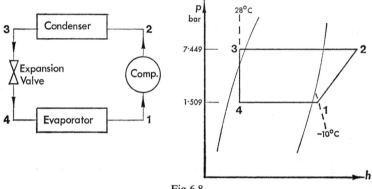

Fig 6.8

Coefficient of performance $= \dfrac{\text{Refrigerating effect}}{\text{work input}}$

$$= \frac{h_1 - h_4}{h_2 - h_1} = \frac{184.74 - 62.64}{214.18 - 184.74} = \frac{122.1}{29.44} = \underline{4.15}$$

$$v_1 = v_g \frac{T_1}{T_{sat}} \text{ approximately}$$

$$v_1 = 0.1088 \times \frac{263}{253} = 0.113 \text{ m}^3/\text{kg}$$

Mass of refrigerant required $= \dfrac{2 \text{ kJ/s}}{122.1 \text{ kJ/kg}} \times \dfrac{60 \text{ s}}{\text{min}} = 0.982$ kg/min

Swept volume required/min $= \dfrac{0.982 \times 0.113}{0.76} = 0.146 \text{ m}^3/\text{min}$

At 600 rev/min this gives the cylinder swept volume

$$= 0.146 \, \frac{m^3}{min} \times \frac{1 \, min}{600} = 0.0243 \times 10^{-2} \, m^3 = \underline{243 \times 10^{-6} \, m}$$

6.9

$$h_6 = h_5 = h_f \text{ at } 30°C = 323.1 \text{ kJ/kg}$$

$$\therefore \quad x_6 = \frac{323.1 - 172.0}{1442.2 - 172.0} = 0.119$$

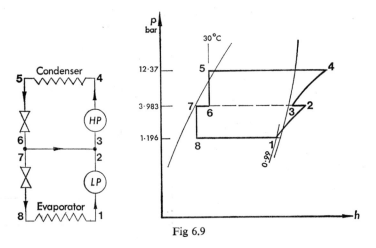

Fig 6.9

$$h_7 = 172 \text{ kJ/kg} = h_8$$

$$h_1 = 1405.6 - 0.01(1405.6 - 44.7) = 1392 \text{ kJ/kg}$$

$$h_1 - h_8 = 1220 \text{ kJ/kg}$$

Mass flow through evaporator for a refrigerating effect of 5 kW

$$= \frac{5 \times 60}{1220} = 0.246 \text{ kg/min}$$

Hence mass flow through condenser $= \dfrac{0.246}{(1 - 0.119)} = \underline{0.28 \text{ kg/min}}$ (

$$s_1 = 5.785 - 0.01(5.785 - 0.188) = 5.729 \text{ kJ/kg K}$$

$$s_2 = s_1$$

$$\therefore \quad h_2 = 1442.2 + \frac{5.729 - 5.365}{5.782 - 5.365}(1564.6 - 1442.2) = \mathbf{1549.2 \text{ kJ/k}}$$

114

Fluid at condition (2) mixes with dry saturated vapour at 3·983 bar from the separator. For 1 kg through the condenser there is 0·119 kg of this vapour to mix with 0·881 kg of superheated vapour.

$$\therefore \quad h_3 = 0.881 \times 1549.2 + 0.119 \times 1442.2 = 1536 \text{ kJ/kg}$$

Similarly $\quad s_3 = 0.881 \times 5.729 + 0.119 \times 5.365 = 5.689 \text{ kJ/kg K}$

$$s_4 = s_1$$

$$\therefore \quad h_4 = 1613.0 + \frac{5.689 - 5.397}{5.731 - 5.397}(1739.3 - 1613.0) = 1724 \text{ kJ/kg}$$

$$\text{Coefficient of performance} = \frac{0.881(h_1 - h_8)}{0.881(h_2 - h_1) + (h_4 - h_3)}$$

$$= \frac{0.881 \times 1220}{0.881 \times 157.2 + 188} = \underline{3.3} \quad \text{(b)}$$

.10

$$h_1 = 3205 \text{ kJ/kg}$$

High pressure turbine

$$\Delta h_s = -205 \text{ kJ/kg} \qquad \therefore \quad \Delta h = 0.76 \Delta h_s = -156 \text{ kJ/kg}$$

$$h_2 = 3049 \text{ kJ/kg}$$

$$h_3 = 3248 \text{ kJ/kg}$$

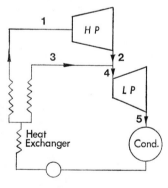
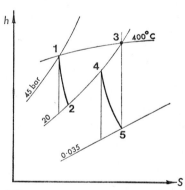

Fig 6.10

The energy balance on mixing gives

$$(0.97 + 0.33)h_4 = 0.33h_3 + 0.97h_2$$

$$\therefore \quad h_4 = 3100 \text{ kJ/kg}$$

Low pressure turbine

$$\Delta h_s = -1040 \text{ kJ/kg} \qquad \Delta h = 0.78 \Delta h_s = -811 \text{ kJ/kg}$$

$$\text{Power} = (0.97 \times 156 + 1.3 \times 811)\frac{10^6}{3600 \times 10^3} = \underline{335 \text{ MW}}$$

$$\text{Cycle efficiency} = \frac{335 \times 3600 \times 10^3}{(3205 \times 0.97 + 0.33 \times 3249 - 1.3 \times 112) 10^6}$$

$$= 0.301 \quad \text{or} \quad \underline{30.1 \text{ per cent}}$$

7

Gaseous Working Fluids

Questions

1. State the conditions necessary for a substance to be defined as a perfect gas.

2. The specific heats of a gas vary linearly with temperature only. Could the gas obey the relation $pv = RT$?

3. The gas described in question (2) undergoes a reversible adiabatic operation. Does it follow the relation $pv^\gamma = $ constant?

4. What do you understand by an air standard cycle?

5. Would you expect the cycle of a modern high speed Diesel engine to approximate to the Diesel air standard cycle?

6. Under what circumstances would you consider using a gas as the working fluid in a refrigeration plant?

7. What is the cause of the rise in pressure when a simple displacement compressor, such as a Roots type, is used?

8. State some factors affecting the volumetric efficiency of a reciprocating compressor.

9. An inefficient turbo-compressor has a high delivery temperature. Is this beneficial in a gas turbine plant?

10. Heat is transferred to a gas flowing at supersonic speed in a constant area duct. Does the flow accelerate or decelerate or is it impossible to say?

Worked Problems

7.1 An ideal air cycle consists of isentropic compression, constant volume heat transfer, isothermal expansion to the original pressure and constant pressure heat transfer to the original temperature. Deduce an expression for the cycle efficiency in terms of the volume compression ratio, r_v, and the isothermal expansion ratio, r_T. In such a cycle the pressure and temperature at the start of compression are 1 bar and 40°C, the compression ratio is 8 and the maximum pressure is 100 bar. Determine the cycle efficiency and the mean effective pressure.

7.2 In an ideal cycle for a compression-ignition (Diesel) engine, the cylinder is assumed to contain 1 kg of air initially at 1·0 bar, 50°C, which is compressed adiabatically through a volume ratio of 16, heated at constant volume until the pressure is 70 bar, further heated at constant pressure and then expanded adiabatically to the initial volume. Finally heat is transferred from the air at constant volume to return it to the initial state. If all the processes are reversible and the heat transfer to the air at constant pressure is equal to that transferred at constant volume, find:
(a) the pressures and temperatures at the cardinal points of the cycle;
(b) the cycle efficiency;
(c) the mean effective pressure of the cycle.

7.3 The pressure and temperature at the beginning of compression in a constant volume air cycle are 1 bar, 30°C, and the compression ratio is 7. The heat transferred to the air is 1700 kJ/kg. Calculate the cycle efficiency and the mean effective pressure assuming that the compression and expansion are isentropic but allowing for the variation in specific heats with temperature.

7.4 A simple gas turbine plant consists of a compressor, turbine and generator on the same shaft. The air leaving the compressor is heated in an exhaust heat exchanger prior to entering the combustion chamber which it leaves at 600°C. The pressure ratio of both compressor and turbine is 4:1 and they each have an isentropic efficiency of 80 per cent. Air enters the compressor at 1·02 bar, 15°C. The heat exchanger has a thermal ratio of 75 per cent.

Assuming the working fluid to be air which may be treated as a perfect gas throughout, calculate the efficiency of the cycle.

7.5 The low pressure compressor of a gas turbine plant is driven by the high pressure turbine and takes in 10 kg/s of air from ambient conditions of 1·15 bar, 19°C. The high pressure compressor is driven by the low pressure turbine and delivers the air at 6 bar. Both compressors have the same stagnation pressure ratio and a polytropic efficiency of 77 per cent. An intercooler reduces the stagnation temperature at entry to the H.P. compressor to 22°C.

There are three turbines in series, the intermediate driving the load. All the turbines have isentropic efficiencies of 80 per cent. The stagnation temperature of the gases entering the H.P. turbine is 700°C. The final exhaust pressure is 1·15 bar and the exhaust heat exchanger has an effectiveness of 78 per cent.

Determine the two intermediate pressures for the turbines, the power output and the cycle efficiency. Treat the fluid as air with constant specific heats throughout.

7.6 Air is used as the working fluid in an aircraft cooling system. It enters the rotary compressor at 1·0 bar, 4°C and is compressed to 3·0 bar with an isentropic efficiency of 72 per cent. The air then passes through a heat exchanger where it is cooled to 55°C, the pressure remaining constant. Expansion then takes place in a turbine to 1·0 bar with an isentropic efficiency of 78 per cent. The low temperature air absorbs a cooling load of 15 kW at constant pressure on flowing through a heat exchanger before re-entering the compressor which is driven by the turbine.

Determine the coefficient of performance of the refrigerator, the driving power required and the air mass flow rate. Treat the air as a perfect gas.

7.7 A displacement compressor deals with 140 m³/min of air at 1·03 bar, 15°C and runs at 3000 rev/min. It has an internal volume compression ratio of 1·2. When the intake conditions are 1·03 bar, 15°C, the delivery pressure is 3 bar.

Determine the driving power required and the isentropic efficiency. The whole process is adiabatic and the internal compression may be taken as reversible.

7.8 A two-stage reciprocating compressor deals with 1 m³/min of free air (1·013 bar, 15°C). The pressure and temperature at beginning of compression are 1·0 bar, 25°C, and the compression and expansion index is 1·3 throughout. The delivery pressure is 16 bar. Both cylinders have clearance volumes of 3 per cent of the swept volume; inter-cooling is at the optimum pressure and cools the air to 25°C. The compressor speed is 400 rev/min.

Determine the swept volume of each cylinder, the driving power required and the volumetric efficiency assuming negligible leakage and a mechanical efficiency of 83 per cent.

7.9 The flow of air into the eye of the impeller of a centrifugal compressor is 5 kg/s in an axial direction, the stagnation pressure and temperature being 1·016 bar, 20°C and the static temperature 10°C. The impeller speed is 16 000 rev/min, its tip diameter 0·5 m, the mean diameter of the eye 0·12 m and the vanes are radial.

Assuming an isentropic efficiency of 76 per cent, a slip factor of 0·9 and treating the air as a perfect gas, determine:

(a) the inner and outer diameters of the eye and the mean angle of bend of the vanes at the eye,

(b) the power absorbed,

(c) the stagnation pressure ratio.

7.10 A perfect gas flows along an insulated pipe of constant cross-sectional area. If friction is *not* negligible, deduce expressions in terms of the Mach number, Ma, for the ratios of the temperatures and pressures at any two points along the flow.

Air is to flow along a pipe having a cross-sectional area of 0·1 m² under the conditions described above. At a particular point the pressure is 1·5 bar, the temperature 20°C and the velocity 200 m/s. Determine for the maximum flow length beyond this point, (a) the values of the pressure, temperature and velocity at the end and (b) the force acting on this length of the pipe.

Unworked Problems

7.11 In an ideal constant volume air standard cycle (Otto cycle) the pressure and temperature at the start of compression are 1·0 bar and 40°C, the compression ratio is 9 and the heat transfer to the air during the constant volume heating process is 2000 kJ/kg. Determine the efficiency of the ideal cycle, the maximum temperature and pressure and the mean effective pressure.

(58·5 per cent; 3540 K; 101·8 bar; 14·66 bar)

7.12 A cycle for a reciprocating engine involves the following reversible processes for air which may be treated as a perfect gas:

(1)–(2) constant volume heat transfer during which the temperature increases from 37°C to 1100°C,

(2)–(3) isothermal expansion through a volume ratio of 5,

(3)–(4) adiabatic expansion through a volume ratio of 2,

(4)–(5) heat transfer at constant pressure to reduce the temperature to the initial value,

(5)–(1) isothermal compression.

Calculate the cycle efficiency and the Carnot efficiency for the same temperature range. (40·5 per cent, 77·4 per cent)

7.13 A 7-litre, 4-stroke compression ignition engine delivers 75 kW at 2000 rev/min when running normally aspirated on an air-fuel ratio of 20:1. The mechanical efficiency is 84 per cent and the volumetric efficiency 75 per cent with ambient air at 1·0 bar, 21°C. The pumping loop mep is 5 per cent of that of the working loop.

When turbo-charged at 1·3 bar the air-fuel ratio is 22:1 and the volumetric efficiency, based on ambient conditions, 100 per cent. As before, the mechanical efficiency is 84 per cent at 2000 rev/min.

Assuming the working loop mep to be proportional to the mass of air induced, estimate the percentage improvement in mep and brake specific fuel consumption when running turbo-charged.

(43·6 per cent, 15·6 per cent)

7.14 An internal combustion engine cycle involves adiabatic compression and expansion, positive heat transfer at constant pressure and negative heat transfer at constant volume. All processes are reversible and the working fluid may be taken as air behaving as a perfect gas. At the start of compression the pressure and temperature are 1·05 bar, 38°C, the compression ratio is 15 and the positive heat transfer is 1860 kJ/kg. Calculate the cycle efficiency and the maximum temperature. (2770 K, 55·8 per cent)

7.15 A slow-speed four-stroke Diesel engine is to be designed to run at 600 rev/min and develop an indicated power of 130 kW when using fuel of gross calorific value 44·2 MJ/kg. The maximum pressure is to be limited to 62 bar and the compression ratio is 14. Assuming that conditions at the start of compression are 1·013 bar, 50°C and that the mass of fuel injected is 1/20 of the mass of air present in the cylinder, estimate a suitable swept volume using an ideal air cycle. The working fluid is air which may be treated as a perfect gas. (0·017 m³)

7.16 A constant volume cycle for an internal combustion engine has a compression ratio of 9 and the energy supply is 1·8 MJ/kg. The temperature and pressure at the start of compression are 25°C and 1·013 bar respectively. Assuming that the working fluid is air having specific heats which are temperature dependent, find the maximum temperature and the cycle efficiency and compare these values with those for the corresponding perfect gas cycle.

(2650 K, 51·4 per cent; 3228 K, 58·5 per cent)

7.17 The pressure and temperature at the start of compression in an ideal dual-combustion cycle are 1·04 bar and 100°C. The pressure at the end of compression is 31·2 bar and the maximum pressure is 52 bar. The heat transfer at constant volume is equal to that at constant pressure. Treat the working fluid as air having the properties represented by the table of Appendix A, calculate the cycle efficiency and the maximum temperature. (2080 K, 52 per cent)

7.18 A turbine is supplied with gas at 6·3 bar, 650°C and exhaust is at 1·05 bar. A simple impulse machine is used running at 19 000 rev/min, having a blade ring of mean diameter 0·36 m with nozzles inclined at 72° to the axis of the machine. Calculate the total area of the throats of the nozzles and the blade angles for zero incidence. Use the following data:

gas mass flow rate 2·2 kg/s, exit velocity axial, nozzle isentropic efficiency 88 per cent, blade velocity coefficient 0·9, $\gamma = 1\cdot4$ $c_p = 1\cdot005$ kJ/kg K. Treat the gas as perfect.

($2\cdot625 \times 10^{-3}$ m², 31·4°, 33·9°)

7.19 A simple gas turbine plant takes in air at 1·015 bar, 18°C, has a pressure ratio of 5 and a polytropic efficiency of 84 per cent for both compression and expansion. The temperature of the gases entering the turbine is 670°C.

Determine the theoretical percentage improvement in specific fuel consumption caused by the addition of an exhaust heat exchanger having a thermal ratio of 75 per cent. Assume $\gamma = 1\cdot4$ throughout

(23·3 per cent)

7.20 The H.P. turbine of a gas turbine plant drives the compressor and the L.P. turbine drives as an alternator giving 1 MW. The L.P. exhaust gas passes through a regenerative heater with a thermal ratio of 0·72. The compressor delivery passes through this heater before entering the combustion chamber where the temperature is raised to 1000 K. The isentropic efficiency of the compressor is 84 per cent, the pressure ratio 7 and inlet conditions are 1·013 bar, 290 K, $\gamma = 1·4$. Both turbines have an isentropic efficiency of 86 per cent and for the gas $c_p = 1·09$ kJ/kg K and $\gamma = 1·36$.

Neglecting the fuel mass determine the cycle efficiency and the air flow in kg/s. (30·4 per cent, 8 kg/s)

7.21 What factors would influence the decision to use an integral or a separate series power turbine in an industrial gas turbine plant? A twin-shaft gas turbine produces 5·2 MW from the L.P. turbine. The compressor is driven by the H.P. turbine and has a pressure ratio of 6. The intake stagnation pressure and temperature are 1·013 bar and 15°C. The L.P. turbine exhausts at 1·013 bar. The stagnation temperature of the gas entering the H.P. turbine is 650°C.

Assume: polytropic efficiency of compressor 87 per cent, isentropic efficiencies of both turbines 85 per cent, fuel of calorific value 43 MJ/kg, an exhaust heat exchanger thermal ratio 0·75, working fluid air with constant specific heats.

Calculate the cycle efficiency and the air mass flow rate.

(26·2 per cent, 58 kg/s)

7.22 The air used in a cooling system enters the centrifugal compressor at 1·0 bar, 18°C. The pressure ratio is 3 and the isentropic efficiency of compression is 72 per cent. After cooling at constant pressure to 20°C the high pressure air is expanded through a turbine to 1·05 bar with an isentropic efficiency of 78 per cent and mixed with warm air at 29°C. The resulting mixture is at 18°C and a proportion of it returns to the compressor.

Determine the mass of warm air that can be mixed with 1 kg of cold air and the performance of the plant. The turbine and compressor are coupled. (5·2 kg, 0·64)

7.23 Describe the basic operation and design of a sliding vane rotary compressor.

A machine of this type deals with 20 m³/min of air at 1·013 bar, 15°C; has a delivery pressure of 7 bar and runs at 1450 rev/min. There is a reversible reduction in air volume of 35 per cent prior to the delivery ports opening when back-flow compression takes place.

Determine the power input required and the isentropic efficiency assuming adiabatic compression. (133·4 kW, 65·5 per cent)

7.24 A two-stage reciprocating compressor draws in 1·3 m³/min of oxygen at 1·38 bar, 15°C and delivers it at 138 bar. Determine the minimum driving power allowing for a mechanical efficiency of 76 per cent and a maximum temperature of 180°C. What is the specific power for this compressor? (22·9 kW; 576 kJ/kg)

7.25 What are the reasons for using more than one stage in a reciprocating compressor?

Deduce an expression for the minimum indicated power of a three-stage compressor having a compression index n where $1 < n < \gamma$. State any other assumptions you make.

If the suction and delivery pressures of such a machine are 1·03 bar and 41·2 bar respectively, evaluate the minimum indicated power required to deal with 1·6 m³/min of air at 1·03 bar, 15°C when $n = 1.32$. (11·8 kW)

7.26 A two-stage single acting air compressor takes in 3·2 m³/min of air at 1·013 bar, 15°C and delivers at 83 bar. The compressor runs at 250 rev/min, has a mean piston speed of 160 m/min, a mechanical efficiency of 80 per cent, a volumetric efficiency of 87 per cent for each stage and a compression and expansion index of 1·3. Find the least power required to drive the machine, the cylinder diameters and the stroke. (38·6 kW; 0·242 m, 0·08 m, 0·32 m)

7.27 Air at ambient conditions of 4·5°C, 0·97 bar, is drawn into the first stage of an axial flow compressor with an axial velocity of 150 m/s. The compressor speed is 13 000 rev/min and it deals with 5 kg/s. The mean diameter of the first stage is 0·4 m and the air angles at entry and exit are 35° and 50° respectively. Determine the blade angles, all angles being relative to the axis of the machine. If the polytropic efficiency of the compressor is 86 per cent and there are 12 stages, estimate the stagnation delivery pressure and the power required to drive the machine.

(48·1°; 32°; 12·53 bar; 1870 kW)

7.28 The air flow into the eye of a centrifugal compressor impeller is at 100 m/s in the axial direction. The following data apply:

impeller speed 800 rev/s; impeller tip diameter 150 mm; eye mean diameter 60 mm; eye annulus radial width 30 mm; slip factor 0·9; static conditions at eye 1 bar, 18°C; isentropic efficiency of impeller 0·89.

Determine (a) the angle of the impeller vanes at the eye mean radius relative to the plane of the impeller;

(b) the stagnation temperature and pressure at the impeller tip.   (33·6°; 423 K; 3·3 bar)

7.29 A pipe has a diameter of 0·2 m. At a point along the pipe air is flowing at a Mach Number of 2·2, the static temperature is 1000°C and the static pressure is 3 bar. If the pipe is thermally insulated find the maximum flow length beyond this point and the stagnation and static pressures and temperatures at the end. Take a friction factor of 0·0112 (that is 4f of Keenan Gas Tables) and treat the air as a perfect gas.   (6·44 m; 16 bar; 8·45 bar; 2505 K; 2088 K)

7.30 A perfect gas having a specific heat ratio, $\gamma = 1·2$, is flowing in a pipe of cross-sectional area 0·1 m^2 with a friction factor of 0·01. Determine the length of pipe between sections where the Mach Number is 0·5 and 0·9, the axial force on this length of pipe and the stagnation and static pressure and temperature at the second point. At the first section the static pressure and temperature are 7 bar and 20°C respectively.

(45·5 m; 163 kN; 6·05 bar, 3·8 bar, 300·3 K; 277·8 K)

Solutions

7.1

$$Q_{2-3} = c_v(T_3 - T_2)$$

$$Q_{3-4} = RT_3 \ln\left(\frac{v_4}{v_3}\right)$$

$$Q_{4-1} = -c_p(T_4 - T_1)$$

$$\eta = \frac{\text{work}}{\text{positive heat transfer}} = \frac{Q_{2-3} + Q_{3-4} + Q_{4-1}}{Q_{2-3} + Q_{3-4}}$$

$$= 1 - \left[\frac{c_p(T_4 - T_1)}{c_v(T_3 - T_2) + RT_3 \ln\left(\frac{v_4}{v_3}\right)}\right]$$

Now
$$T_2 = T_1\left(\frac{v_1}{v_2}\right)^{\gamma-1} = T_1(r_v)^{\gamma-1}$$

$$T_3 = T_4 = T_1\left(\frac{v_4}{v_1}\right) = T_1\left(\frac{v_4}{v_3}\right)\left(\frac{v_3}{v_1}\right) = T_1\left(\frac{r_T}{r_v}\right)$$

125

$$\therefore \quad \eta = 1 - \left\{ \frac{c_p T_1\left[\left(\dfrac{r_T}{r_v}\right) - 1\right]}{c_v T_1\left[\left(\dfrac{r_T}{r_v}\right) - (r_v)^{\gamma-1}\right] + R T_1\left(\dfrac{r_T}{r_v}\right)\ln r_T} \right\}$$

from which T_1 may be cancelled.

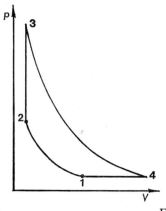
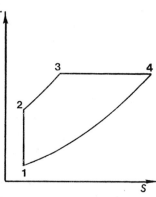

Fig 7.1

Now $\qquad r_v = 8 \quad \text{and} \quad r_T = \dfrac{v_4}{v_3} = \dfrac{p_3}{p_4} = \dfrac{100}{1}$

$$\therefore \quad \eta = 1 - \left[\frac{1 \cdot 005\left[\dfrac{100}{8} - 1\right]}{0 \cdot 718\left[\dfrac{100}{8} - 8^{\frac{1}{2 \cdot 5}}\right] + 0 \cdot 2871 \times \dfrac{100}{8}\ln 100} \right]$$

$$= 0 \cdot 515 \quad \text{or} \quad \underline{51 \cdot 5 \text{ per cent}}$$

Note that $T_3 = 313 \times 12 \cdot 5 = 3913$ K.

The Carnot efficiency for this temperature range $= \dfrac{3913 - 313}{3913} = 0 \cdot 9$

$$\text{mep} = \frac{\text{work}}{\text{swept volume}}$$

$$= \frac{T_1\left\{ c_v\left[\left(\dfrac{r_T}{r_v}\right) - r_v^{\gamma-1}\right] + R\left(\dfrac{r_T}{r_v}\right)\ln r_T - c_p\left[\left(\dfrac{r_T}{r_v}\right) - 1\right] \right\}}{\dfrac{v_1}{8}(r_T - 1)}$$

and
$$v_1 = \frac{RT_1}{p_1} = \frac{0.2871 \times 313}{10^2} = 0.898 \text{ m}^3/\text{kg}$$

Hence mep $= 345 \text{ kN/m}^2 = \underline{3.45 \text{ bar.}}$

7.2

$$T_1 = 323 \text{ K} \qquad T_2 = T_1\left(\frac{v_1}{v_2}\right)^{\gamma-1} = 323\,(16)^{\frac{1}{2.5}} = \underline{979 \text{ K}}$$

$$p_2 = p_1\left(\frac{v_1}{v_2}\right)^{\gamma} = 1.0\,(16)^{1.4} = \underline{48.5 \text{ bar}}$$

$$T_3 = T_2\frac{p_3}{p_2} = 979 \times \frac{70}{48.5} = \underline{1413 \text{ K}}$$

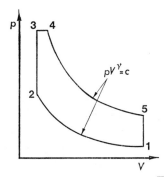
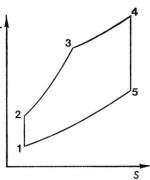

Fig 7.2

$$Q_{2-3} = c_v(T_3 - T_2) = 0.718 \times 434 = 312 \text{ kJ/kg}$$

$$Q_{3-4} = Q_{2-3} = c_p(T_4 - T_3)$$

$$\therefore \quad T_4 = \frac{312}{1.005} + 1413 = \underline{1723 \text{ K}}$$

$$\frac{v_4}{v_3} = \frac{T_4}{T_3} = 1.219$$

$$\therefore \quad \frac{v_5}{v_4} = \frac{v_5}{v_2}\frac{v_2}{v_4} = \frac{16}{1.219} = 13.12$$

$$\therefore \quad T_5 = T_4\left(\frac{v_4}{v_5}\right)^{\gamma-1} = \frac{1723}{(13.12)^{0.4}} = \underline{615 \text{ K}}$$

$$p_5 = p_1\left(\frac{T_5}{T_1}\right) = 1.0 \times \frac{615}{323} = \underline{1.9 \text{ bar}}$$

Cycle efficiency $= \dfrac{\text{work}}{\text{heat transfer to air}}$

$$= 1 - \left[\frac{c_v(T_5 - T_1)}{c_v(T_3 - T_2) + c_p(T_4 - T_3)}\right]$$

$$= 1 - \frac{0 \cdot 718(615 - 323)}{624} = 0 \cdot 664 \quad \text{or} \quad \underline{66 \cdot 4 \text{ per cen}}$$

$$\text{mep} = \frac{\text{work}}{\text{swept volume}} = \frac{\text{efficiency} \times \text{heat transfer}}{\frac{15}{16} \times v_1}$$

$$v_1 = \frac{RT_1}{p_1} = \frac{0 \cdot 2871 \times 323}{10^2} = 0 \cdot 927 \text{ m}^3/\text{kg}$$

$$\text{mep} = \frac{0 \cdot 6635 \times 624}{0 \cdot 927 \times \dfrac{15}{16}} = 476 \text{ kN/m}^2 \quad \text{or} \quad \underline{4 \cdot 76 \text{ bar}}$$

7.3 To allow for the variation of the properties of air with temperature we could use mean values based on the air table of the Mayhew and Rogers tables, involving a trial and error solution. We shall make use of the table of standardised enthalpy and absolute entropy for air given in Appendix A. Using this table we can plot the constant pressure line, s_{p0}, on a T–s diagram (fig 7.3(a)) and add to it the volume line, s_{v0} which passes through the point p_0 at 300 K.

Then
$$s_{v0} = s_{p0} - R_0 \ln \frac{T}{300}$$

We can also plot the enthalpy for air on a temperature energy diagram (Fig 7.3(b)) and add a line representing $R_0 T$.

Then
$$u = h - R_0 T$$

This diagram could be superimposed on the T–s diagram.

Provided that we do not require absolute entropies but only differences we may now regard p_0(or v_0) as any suitable value and consider other pressure lines relative to it. Note that if absolute values are required then p_0 is $1 \cdot 013$ bar for the data of the table.

Let point (1) at 1 bar, 30°C be fixed on the s_{v0} line at 303 K. The $u_1 = -2 \cdot 4$ MJ/kg mole.

Now the compression (1) to (2) is isentropic and point (2) is a *horizontal* distance, x

where $\qquad x = -R_0 \ln \dfrac{v_1}{v_2}$ from the s_{v0} line.

This value is the change of entropy at constant temperature for the known volume ratio.

Thus $\qquad x = -8.3143 \ln 7 = -16.12$ kJ/kg mole K
and point (2) may be located giving $T_2 = 660$ K and
$u_2 = 5$ MJ/kg mole.

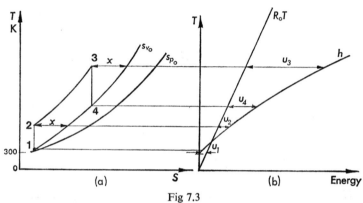

Fig 7.3

The constant volume heat transfer is

$$1.7 \text{ MJ/kg} = 1.7 \times 28.96 = 49.1 \text{ MJ/kg mole}$$

$$\therefore \quad u_3 = 49.1 + 5 = 54.1 \text{ MJ/kg mole}$$

Point (3) is also distant x from s_{v0} hence $T_3 = 2500$ K.
(3) to (4) is isentropic and (4) lies on s_{v0} since $v_4 = v_1$

$$\therefore \quad T_4 = 1400 \text{ K and } u_4 = 23.2 \text{ MJ/kg mole}$$

The heat transfer (4) to (1) $= u_1 - u_4 = -25.6$ MJ/kg mole

$$\text{Cycle efficiency} = \frac{\text{work}}{\text{heat supplied}} = \frac{\sum Q}{Q_{2-3}} = \frac{Q_{2-3} + Q_{4-1}}{Q_{2-3}}$$

$$= 1 - \frac{25.6}{49.1} = 0.478 \quad \text{or} \quad \underline{47.8 \text{ per cent}}$$

$$v_1 = \frac{R_0 T_1}{p_1} = \frac{8.3143 \times 303}{100} = 25.2 \text{ m}^3/\text{kg mole}$$

$$\text{mep} = \frac{\text{work}}{\text{swept volume}} = \frac{49 \cdot 1 - 25 \cdot 6}{\dfrac{6}{7} \times 25 \cdot 2} = 1 \cdot 086 \text{ MN/m}^2 = \underline{10 \cdot 86 \text{ bar.}}$$

7.4

$$T_1 = 288 \text{ K}$$

$$T_{2s} = 288 (4)^{\frac{\gamma-1}{\gamma}} \text{ where } \gamma = 1 \cdot 4 \qquad T_{2s} = 428 \text{ K}$$

$$\Delta T_s = 140 \text{ K} \qquad \Delta T = \frac{\Delta T_s}{\eta_s} = \frac{140}{0 \cdot 8} = 175 \text{ K}$$

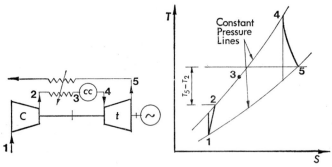

Fig 6.4

$$T_2 = 288 + 175 = 463 \text{ K}$$

$$T_4 = 873 \text{ K}$$

$$T_{5s} = \frac{873}{4^{\frac{\gamma-1}{\gamma}}} = 588 \text{ K}$$

$$\Delta T_s = -285 \text{ K} \qquad \Delta T = -285 \times 0 \cdot 8 = -228 \text{ K}$$

$$T_5 = 873 - 228 = 645 \text{ K}$$

Available ΔT for heat exchanger $= T_5 - T_2 = 182 \text{ K}$

$$\therefore \quad T_3 - T_2 = 0 \cdot 75 \times 182 = 136 \cdot 5 \text{ K and } T_3 = 600 \text{ K}$$

Assuming both turbine and compressor to be adiabatic, the steady flow energy equation gives:

$$-W = \Delta h = c_p \Delta T$$

But c_p is constant throughout in this case and net work is

$$c_p\left[\underbrace{\Delta T}_{\text{turbine}} + \underbrace{\Delta T}_{\text{compressor}}\right]$$

and similarly from the energy equation for the combustion chamber

$$Q = c_p(T_4 - T_3)$$

Then efficiency $= \dfrac{(T_4 - T_5) - (T_2 - T_1)}{(T_4 - T_3)} = \dfrac{228 - 175}{273}$

$$= 0.1945 \quad \text{or} \quad \underline{19.45 \text{ per cent.}}$$

.5

$$T_{01} = 292 \text{ K}$$

$$\eta_{\text{pol}} = \left(\frac{\gamma - 1}{\gamma}\right)\frac{\ln\left(\dfrac{p_2}{p_1}\right)}{\ln\left(\dfrac{T_2}{T_1}\right)} = \frac{\ln\left(\dfrac{6}{1 \cdot 15}\right)^{\frac{1}{4}}}{3 \cdot 5 \ln\left(\dfrac{T_2}{T_1}\right)}$$

whence $\quad \dfrac{T_2}{T_1} = 1.36 \qquad T_2 = 397 \text{ K} \qquad \Delta T_{c1} = 105 \text{ K.}$

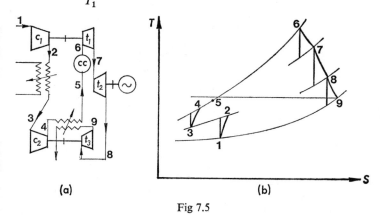

Fig 7.5

Since η_{pol} and pressure ratio are the same for the H.P. compressor, the temperature ratio is the same and $T_4 = 1.36 T_3 = 1.36 \times 295 = 401$ K.

$$\Delta T_{c2} = 106 \text{ K}$$

Since the LP compressor is driven by the H.P. turbine and the value of c_p is assumed constant

$$T_6 - T_7 = \Delta T_{c1} = 105K \text{ and } T_7 = 973 - 105 = 868 \text{ K.}$$

$$T_6 - T_{7s} = \frac{105}{0 \cdot 8} = 131 \text{ K.}$$

$$\therefore \quad T_{7s} = 842 \text{ K.}$$

$$\therefore \quad \frac{p_6}{p_7} = \left(\frac{973}{842}\right)^{\frac{\gamma}{\gamma - 1}} = 1 \cdot 67 \qquad p_7 = \underline{3 \cdot 59 \text{ bar.}}$$

Again $T_8 - T_9 = 106 \text{ K}$ since H.P. compressor is driven by L.P. turbine.

$$\therefore \quad T_8 - T_{9s} = \frac{106}{0 \cdot 8} = 132 \cdot 5 \text{ K.} \qquad T_8 = 132 \cdot 5 + T_{9s} \qquad (i)$$

Also $T_7 - T_8 = 0 \cdot 8(T_7 - T_{8s})$

$$\therefore \quad 0 \cdot 8 T_{8s} = T_8 - 0 \cdot 2 \times 868 = T_{9s} - 41 \cdot 1$$

$$T_{8s} = \frac{T_{9s}}{0 \cdot 8} - 51 \cdot 38 \qquad (ii)$$

$$\frac{p_8}{p_9} = \left(\frac{T_8}{T_{9s}}\right)^{3 \cdot 5} \quad \text{and} \quad \frac{p_7}{p_8} = \left(\frac{T_7}{T_{8s}}\right)^{3 \cdot 5}$$

$$\therefore \quad \frac{p_7}{p_9} = \left(\frac{T_7 T_8}{T_{9s} T_{8s}}\right)^{3 \cdot 5}$$

Using (i) and (ii) $\dfrac{3 \cdot 59}{1 \cdot 15} = \left[\dfrac{868 (132 \cdot 5 + T_{9s})}{T_{9s}(1 \cdot 25 T_{9s} - 51 \cdot 38)}\right]^{3 \cdot 5}$

Whence $\qquad T_{9s} = 644 \text{ K}$ and $T_8 = 777 \text{ K}$ from (i)

$$\therefore \quad T_7 - T_8 = 868 - 777 = 91 \text{ K}$$

$$T_9 = 671 \text{ K} \qquad T_{8s} = 756 \text{ K} \qquad p_8 = \underline{2 \cdot 22 \text{ bar}}$$

Power output $= 1 \cdot 005 \times 10 \times 91 = 914 \text{ kW}$

$$T_5 - T_4 = 0 \cdot 78(T_9 - T_4) = 0 \cdot 78(671 - 401) = 210 \text{ K}$$

$$T_5 = 612 \text{ K}$$

$$T_6 - T_5 = 973 - 612 = 361 \text{ K}$$

$$\text{Efficiency} = \frac{91}{361} \times 100 = \underline{25 \cdot 2 \text{ per cent}}$$

7.6

$$T_{2s} = T_1\left(\frac{p_2}{p_1}\right)^{\frac{\gamma-1}{\gamma}} = 277\,(3)^{\frac{1}{3\cdot5}} = 379\ \text{K}$$

$$\therefore \quad T_{2s} - T_1 = 102\ \text{K} \qquad T_2 - T_1 = \frac{102}{0\cdot72} = 141\cdot8\ \text{K}$$

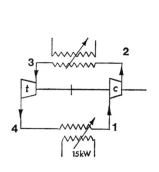
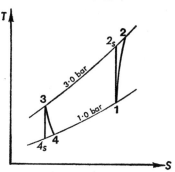

Fig 7.6

$$T_3 = 328\ \text{K}$$

$$T_{4s} = T_3\left(\frac{p_4}{p_3}\right)^{\frac{\gamma-1}{\gamma}} = \frac{328}{1\cdot368} = 240\ \text{K}$$

$$\therefore \quad T_3 - T_{4s} = 88\ \text{K} \quad \text{and} \quad T_3 - T_4 = 88 \times 0\cdot78 = 68\cdot6\ \text{K}$$

$$T_4 = 259\cdot4\ \text{K}$$

Refrigerating effect $= c_p(T_1 - T_4) = c_p17\cdot6$ for unit mass

Net work input $= c_p[(T_2 - T_1) - (T_3 - T_4)]$ for unit mass

$$\text{Coefficient of performance} = \frac{c_p17\cdot6}{c_p73\cdot2} = \underline{0\cdot24}$$

$$\text{Power required} = \frac{15}{0\cdot24} = \underline{62\cdot3\ \text{kW}}$$

$$\text{Mass flow rate} = \frac{15}{1\cdot005 \times 73\cdot2} = \underline{0\cdot204\ \text{kg/s}}$$

7.7

Let the processes a–1 and 3–c represent the displacements during inflow and delivery respectively. Then process 1–2 represents the isentropic internal compression for which pv^γ = constant and 2–1 represents the irreversible back-flow compression when the delivery ports open.

$$p_2 = p_1\left(\frac{V_1}{V_2}\right)^\gamma = 1{\cdot}03\,(1{\cdot}2)^{1{\cdot}4} = 1{\cdot}33$$

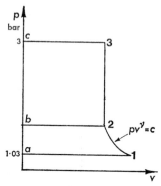

Fig 7.7

Work done, represented by the area a 1 2 b

$$= \left(\frac{\gamma}{\gamma-1}\right)p_1V_1\left[\left(\frac{p_2}{p_1}\right)^{\frac{\gamma-1}{\gamma}} - 1\right] = \dot{W}_1$$

where $\qquad V_1 = 140\ \mathrm{m^3/min} = 2{\cdot}33\ \mathrm{m^3/s}$

$\qquad\quad \dot{W}_1 = 63{\cdot}8\ \mathrm{kW}$

Work $\qquad \dot{W}_2 = \mathrm{b}\,2\,3\,\mathrm{c} = (p_3 - p_2)V_2 = (p_3 - p_2)\dfrac{V_1}{1{\cdot}2}$

$$= (3 - 1{\cdot}33)10^2 \times \frac{2{\cdot}33}{1{\cdot}2} = 324\ \mathrm{kW}$$

Total power $= \dot{W}_1 + \dot{W}_2 = \underline{387{\cdot}8\ \mathrm{kW}}$

If the whole compression were isentropic

$$\dot{W} = \left(\frac{\gamma}{\gamma-1}\right)p_1V_1\left[\left(\frac{p_3}{p_1}\right)^{\frac{\gamma-1}{\gamma}} - 1\right] = 300\ \mathrm{kW}$$

Isentropic efficiency $= \dfrac{\text{isentropic power}}{\text{actual power}}$

$$= \frac{300}{387{\cdot}8} = 0{\cdot}773 \quad\text{or}\quad \underline{77{\cdot}3\ \text{per cent}}$$

7.8

Since the intercooler pressure is that for minimum work

$$p_2 = (p_1 p_3)^{\frac{1}{2}} = (1 \times 16)^{\frac{1}{2}} = 4 \text{ bar}$$

Each cylinder has the same pressure ratio

$$\frac{p_2}{p_1} = \frac{p_3}{p_2} = \left(\frac{p_3}{p_1}\right)^{\frac{1}{2}}$$

and since $T_3 = T_1$ the work required by each will be the same.

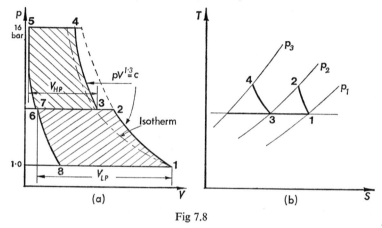

Fig 7.8

The work required to deal with unit mass will not be affected by the clearance which merely reduces the mass dealt with per cycle. This will be evident if the compressor is considered as part of a steady flow system where the work is clearly dependent on the mass flow through the system.

$$\text{Work} = \left(\frac{2n}{n-1}\right) R T_1 \left[\left(\frac{p_3}{p_1}\right)^{\frac{n-1}{2n}} - 1\right]$$

$$= \frac{2 \times 1 \cdot 3}{0 \cdot 3} \times 0 \cdot 2871 \times 298 \left[16^{\frac{0 \cdot 3}{2 \cdot 6}} - 1\right] = 279 \text{ kJ/kg}$$

$$\text{Mass flow rate} = \frac{pV}{RT} = \frac{1 \cdot 013 \times 10^2 \times 1}{0 \cdot 2871 \times 288} = 1 \cdot 224 \text{ kg/min}$$

$$\text{Driving power} = \frac{1 \cdot 224}{60} \frac{\text{kg}}{\text{s}} \times 279 \frac{\text{kJ}}{\text{kg}} \times \frac{1}{0 \cdot 83} = \underline{6 \cdot 87 \text{ kW}}$$

Volume of air drawn in at conditions obtaining at the start of compression is

$$(V_1 - V_8) = 1.224 \frac{kg}{min} \times \frac{RT_1}{p_1} \times \frac{1}{400} \frac{min}{cycles}$$

$$= 2.615 \times 10^{-3} \text{ m}^3/\text{cycle}$$

$$V_8 = V_6\left(\frac{p_6}{p_7}\right)^{\frac{1}{n}} = 0.03V_{LP} \times 2.91 = 0.0873V_{LP}$$

$$(V_1 - V_8) = (1.03 - 0.0873)V_{LP} = 0.9427 \ V_{LP}$$

$$V_{LP} = \underline{2.775 \times 10^{-3} \text{ m}^3}$$

Since the percentage clearance is the same in both cylinders

$$V_{HP} = V_{LP}\left(\frac{p_2}{p_1}\right) = \frac{V_{LP}}{4} = \underline{0.6938 \times 10^{-3} \text{ m}^3}$$

$$\text{Volumetric efficiency} = \frac{\text{volume of free air per cycle}}{\text{LP swept volume}}$$

$$= \frac{1}{400} \times \frac{10^3}{2.775} = 0.90 \quad \text{or} \quad \underline{90 \text{ per cent}}$$

7.9

At entry the difference between the stagnation and static temperatures is 10 K

$$\therefore \quad v_1^2 = 2 \times 10 \text{ K} \times 1.005 \frac{m \text{ kN}}{kg \text{ K}} \times \frac{10^3 \text{ kg m}}{kN \text{ s}^2}$$

$$\therefore \quad v_1^2 = 20.1 \times 10^3 \ (m/s)^2$$

$$v_1 = 142 \text{ m/s}$$

$$v_{b1} = \pi \times 0.12 \times \frac{16\,000}{60} = 100.5 \text{ m/s}$$

Referring to fig 7.9(a)

$$(90 - \alpha) = \tan^{-1}\frac{142}{100.5} = 54.7°$$

$$\alpha = \underline{35.3°} \tag{a}$$

$$\dot{m} = \rho_1 v_1 A_1 \qquad \rho_1 = \frac{p_1}{RT_1}$$

$$\frac{p_1}{p_{01}} = \left(\frac{T_1}{T_{01}}\right)^{\frac{\gamma}{\gamma-1}} = \left(\frac{283}{293}\right)^{3\cdot5} = \frac{1}{1\cdot129}$$

$$\therefore \quad p_1 = \frac{1\cdot016}{1\cdot129} = 0\cdot9 \text{ bar}$$

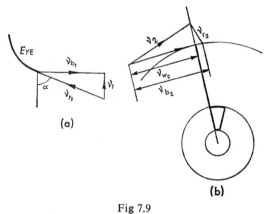

Fig 7.9

$$\rho_1 = \frac{0\cdot9 \times 10^2}{0\cdot2871 \times 283} = 1\cdot107 \text{ kg/m}^3$$

$$A_1 = \frac{5}{1\cdot107 \times 142} = 0\cdot0318 \text{ m}^2 \qquad (i)$$

Now
$$A_1 = \frac{\pi(d_0^2 - d_i^2)}{4} \qquad (ii)$$

and
$$\frac{d_0 + d_i}{2} = 0\cdot12 \text{ m}$$

$$d_0 = 0\cdot24 - d_i \qquad (iii)$$

Using (i) (ii) and (iii) gives $\underline{d_0 = 0\cdot204 \text{ m}}$ \qquad (a)

$$\underline{d_i = 0\cdot036 \text{ m}}$$

Power $= \dot{m}(v_{p2}v_{w2} - v_{p1}v_{w1})$

and v_{w1}, the inlet whirl velocity $= 0$

$$\therefore \quad \text{power} = \dot{m}\sigma v_{p2}^2 \qquad \text{see fig 7·9(b)}$$

137

$$\text{where the slip factor } \sigma = \frac{v_{w2}}{v_{p2}}$$

$$\text{Power} = 5 \times 0 \cdot 9 \times \left[\pi \times 0 \cdot 5 \times \frac{16\,000}{60} \right]^2 = 4 \cdot 5 \times 418^2$$

$$= 788\,000 \text{ W} = \underline{788 \text{ kW}} \qquad \text{(b)}$$

$$\text{Also Power} = \dot{m}c_p\Delta T_0 = 5 \times 1 \cdot 005 \times \Delta T_0 = 788$$

$$\therefore \quad \Delta T_0 = 156 \cdot 5 \text{ K and } \Delta T_{0s} = 156 \cdot 5 \times 0 \cdot 76 = 119 \text{ K}$$

$$T_{02s} = 293 + 119 = 412 \text{ K}$$

$$\frac{p_{02}}{p_{01}} = \left(\frac{T_{02s}}{T_{01}} \right)^{\frac{\gamma}{\gamma - 1}} = \left(\frac{412}{293} \right)^{3 \cdot 5} = \underline{3 \cdot 3} \qquad \text{(c)}$$

7.10 If the stagnation enthalpy at any point is h_0, then

$$(h_0 - h) = \frac{v^2}{2} - 0$$

For a perfect gas this becomes $c_p(T_0 - T) = \dfrac{v^2}{2}$

But $\qquad c_p = \left(\dfrac{\gamma}{\gamma - 1} \right)R \qquad \therefore \quad \dfrac{2\gamma RT}{(\gamma - 1)}\left(\dfrac{T_0}{T} - 1 \right) = v^2$

But $\gamma RT = a^2$ where a is the local sonic velocity

and the Mach Number, $\qquad Ma = \dfrac{v}{a}$

Hence $Ma^2 = \left(\dfrac{2}{\gamma - 1} \right)\left(\dfrac{T_0}{T} - 1 \right)$ and $\dfrac{T_0}{T} = 1 + \left(\dfrac{\gamma - 1}{2} \right)Ma^2$ (i)

$$\therefore \quad T = \frac{T_0}{1 + \left(\dfrac{\gamma - 1}{2} \right)Ma^2}$$

Differentiating

$$dT = \frac{dT_0\left[1 + \left(\dfrac{\gamma - 1}{2} \right)Ma^2 \right] - T_0 d\left[1 + \left(\dfrac{\gamma - 1}{2} \right)Ma^2 \right]}{\left[1 + \left(\dfrac{\gamma - 1}{2} \right)Ma^2 \right]^2}$$

The process being considered is adiabatic and no work transfers are involved so that the total energy, and hence T_0, is constant.

$$\therefore \quad dT_0 = 0$$

and using (i)

$$\frac{dT}{T} = -\frac{d\left[1 + \left(\frac{\gamma - 1}{2}\right)Ma^2\right]}{\left[1 + \left(\frac{\gamma - 1}{2}\right)Ma^2\right]} \qquad (ii)$$

Integrating

$$\frac{T_2}{T_1} = \frac{\left[1 + \left(\frac{\gamma - 1}{2}\right)Ma_1^2\right]}{\left[1 + \left(\frac{\gamma - 1}{2}\right)Ma_2^2\right]} \qquad (iii)$$

Using the continuity equation $v\rho A = $ constant, we have on differentiating

$$\rho v dA + \rho A dv + v A d\rho = 0$$

$$\therefore \quad \frac{dA}{A} + \frac{dv}{v} + \frac{d\rho}{\rho} = 0 \qquad (iv)$$

In this case $dA = 0$ and for a perfect gas $\rho = \dfrac{p}{RT}$

$$\therefore \quad d\rho = \frac{1}{R}[-pT^{-2}dT + dpT^{-1}]$$

$$\therefore \quad \frac{d\rho}{\rho} = \left[\frac{dp}{p} - \frac{dT}{T}\right]$$

also

$$\frac{dv}{v} = \frac{d[Ma(\gamma RT)^{\frac{1}{2}}]}{Ma(\gamma RT)^{\frac{1}{2}}} = \frac{dMa}{Ma} + \tfrac{1}{2}\frac{dT}{T}$$

Substituting these values in (iv)

$$\frac{dp}{p} + \frac{dMa}{Ma} - \tfrac{1}{2}\frac{dT}{T} = 0 \qquad (v)$$

Using (ii)

$$\frac{dp}{p} = -\tfrac{1}{2}\frac{d\left[1 + \left(\frac{\gamma - 1}{2}\right)Ma^2\right]}{1 + \left(\frac{\gamma - 1}{2}\right)Ma^2} - \frac{dMa}{Ma} \qquad (vi)$$

Integrating (vi)

$$\frac{p_2}{p_1} = \frac{Ma_1}{Ma_2}\left[\frac{1 + \left(\frac{\gamma - 1}{2}\right)Ma_1^2}{1 + \left(\frac{\gamma - 1}{2}\right)Ma_2^2}\right]^{\frac{1}{2}} \qquad (vii)$$

(iii) and (vii) are the required expressions.

The flow will choke when $Ma_2 = 1$ for which condition, denoted by subscript c, (*iii*) becomes

$$\frac{T_c}{T_1} = \frac{\left[1 + \left(\frac{\gamma - 1}{2}\right)Ma_1^2\right]}{1 + \left(\frac{\gamma - 1}{2}\right)}$$

$$a_1^2 = \gamma RT_1 = 1 \cdot 4 \times 0 \cdot 2871 \frac{kJ}{kg\ K} \times 293\ K \times 10^3 \frac{kg\ m^2}{s^2\ kJ}$$

$$= 117 \cdot 8 \times 10^3 \left(\frac{m}{s}\right)^2$$

$$\therefore \quad Ma_1^2 = \left(\frac{v}{a}\right)^2 = \frac{4 \times 10^4}{117 \cdot 8 \times 10^3} = 0 \cdot 34 \quad \therefore \quad Ma_1 = 0 \cdot 583$$

$$\therefore \quad T_c = \frac{293(1 + 0 \cdot 2 \times 0 \cdot 34)}{1 \cdot 2} = \underline{260 \cdot 5\ K}$$

From (*vii*)
$$\frac{p_c}{p_1} = 0 \cdot 583\left[\frac{1 + 0 \cdot 2 \times 0 \cdot 34}{1 \cdot 2}\right]^{\frac{1}{2}}$$

$$p_c = \underline{0 \cdot 824\ bar}$$

$$v_c^2 = a_c^2 = \gamma RT_c = 1 \cdot 4 \times 0 \cdot 2871 \times 260 \cdot 5 \times 10^3 = 104 \cdot 8 \times 10^3$$

$$v_c = \underline{324\ m/s}$$

The force acting on the tube in the direction of fluid flow will be given by

$$F = \dot{m}(v_1 - v_c) + A(p_1 - p_c)$$

$$\dot{m} = \rho vA = \frac{p}{RT}vA = \left[\frac{1 \cdot 5 \times 10^2}{0 \cdot 2871 \times 293}\right]\frac{kg}{m^3} \times 200 \frac{m}{s} \times 0 \cdot 1\ m^2$$

$$= 35 \cdot 65\ kg/s$$

$$F = 35 \cdot 65 \frac{kg}{s} \times -124 \frac{m}{s} \times 10^{-3} \frac{kN\ s^2}{kg\ m} + 0 \cdot 1\ m^2 \times 67 \cdot 6 \frac{kN}{m^2}$$

$$= \underline{2 \cdot 34\ kN}$$

8

Heat Transfer

Questions

1. Distinguish between the conduction, convection and radiation modes of heat transfer.

2. Is a material medium necessary for heat transfer by radiation?

3. What is the difference between natural and forced convection?

4. Is it better to arrange for the flow in a heat exchanger tube to be laminar or turbulent?

5. Write the Fourier rate equation for heat transfer by conduction.

6. What is the significance of the Reynolds number in heat transfer?

7. Why are gases generally poor conductors?

8. Why are liquid metals, such as sodium and potassium excellent heat transfer fluids?

9. Explain how the temperature in an unheated greenhouse can be higher than the ambient temperature.

0. Under what conditions would the addition of thermal insulation material to a tube cause an increase in heat transfer from the tube?

Worked Problems

.1 A low temperature storage chamber is maintained at $-20°C$. The interior dimensions are $10 \text{ m} \times 8 \text{ m} \times 2·5 \text{ m}$ high. The walls and ceiling consist of board 50 mm thick on the inside, 80 mm of insulation with 250 mm of concrete on the outside. The thermal conductivities of the board, insulation and concrete are respectively 0·2, 0·04 and 1·8 W/m K.

Determine the inward heat flow when the outer surface of the concrete is at 20°C. The flow through the floor may be neglected.

8.2 A steel pipe having a diameter of 150 mm carries saturated steam at 46 bar and is lagged with a layer of material 100 mm thick of thermal conductivity 0·05 W/m K. Outside this is a further layer 40 mm thick of conductivity 0·1 W/m K which has a surface heat transfer coefficient of 8 W/m² K. The ambient temperature is 18°C. Calculate the condensation rate for a 100 m length of pipe assuming that the thermal resistance of the steel pipe and all other internal resistances are negligible.

8.3 A cylindrical vessel with flat ends contains a fluid at 100°C and is insulated with 100 mm thickness of material of thermal conductivity 0·04 W/m K, and surface coefficient 10 W/m² K. The surroundings are at 15°C. If the volume enclosed is 10 m³ and the length of the cylinder is four times its internal diameter, find the rate of heat transfer. The resistance of the vessel may be neglected.

What dimensions would be required for a spherical vessel to hold the same quantity of the fluid if lagged with the same material to give the same rate of heat transfer?

8.4 (a) A thin walled vertical duct of circular cross-section carries gas at 194°C. The duct is 0·4 m in diameter and the surrounding air may be considered as 'still', at 10°C. Determine the heat transfer rate from a length of 1 m of the duct assuming that boundary layer flow is laminar, the heat transfer coefficient being given by

$$h = 1·37\left(\frac{\Delta T}{L}\right)^{0·25}$$

where h is in W/m² K, T in K and L in m.

(b) The general non-dimensional correlation for laminar flow natural convection for a large vertical cylinder is

$$\frac{hL}{k} = 0·56\left[\frac{L^3\beta g\Delta T\rho^2}{\mu^2}\right]^{0·25}\left[\frac{\mu c_p}{k}\right]^{0·25}$$

Compare the value of h from this expression with the simplified equation in (a). The fluid properties are to be evaluated at film temperature which is defined as the average of the bulk fluid and wall temperatures.

3.5 At a point in a tube through which air is flowing the pressure and temperature are 1·3 bar and 52°C. The tube has an internal diameter of 0·1 m and the air flow rate is 0·02 kg/s. The tube wall temperature is 100°C. Determine the rate of heat transfer for a length of 1 m in the region of this point. The correlation

$$\text{Nu} = 0.023\ \text{Re}^{0.8}\ \text{Pr}^{0.4}$$

may be used for turbulent flow in tubes where the fluid properties are evaluated at the bulk temperature.

3.6 An enclosure measures 1·5 m × 1·75 m with a height of 2 m. The walls and ceiling are maintained at 250°C and the floor at 130°C. The walls and ceiling have an emissivity of 0·82 and the floor 0·7. Determine the net radiation to the floor.

3.7 A rectangular copper conductor has a cross-section of 80 mm × 5 mm and carries a current of 6000 amp. The conductor rests in a trough of insulation so that the heat transfer from one face and both edges is negligible. The other face is bare and is found to have a steady temperature of 50°C.

Determine the maximum temperature in the bar and where this occurs.

Also find the temperature at the centre of the bar.

For copper $k = 380$ W/m K and resistivity $\rho = 2 \times 10^{-8}$ Ω m.

3.8 A wall of rectangular cross-section 1 m thick, is made from a material having a thermal conductivity of 0·05 W/m K, a density of 237 kg/m³ and $c_p = 0.6$ kJ/kg K. The wall is not in a steady thermal state but at a particular instant thermocouple readings suggest a temperature distribution given by

$$T = (-120x^3 - 15x + 300)°C$$

Calculate the rate of change of temperature at the faces of the wall and at the mid-section, and the rate of energy increase of the wall expressed per unit area of wall face.

3.9 Oil is cooled by water in a counter flow heat exchanger. The oil flow rate is 2000 kg/h, entering at 107°C and leaving at 30°C. Its mean $c_p = 2.51$ kJ/kg K. The water enters at 15°C and its exit temperature is not to exceed 80°C. The overall heat transfer coefficient is expected to be 1·5 kW/m² K.

Determine the water flow rate, the surface area required and the effectiveness of the heat exchanger.

8.10 Air is heated whilst flowing steadily through a duct having a constant cross-sectional area of 0·03 m². The static conditions at inlet are 120°C, 4 bar with a velocity of 174·8 m/s. Find the heat transfer rate required to give an exit Mach number of 0·9 and the static conditions at this point.

What is the maximum static temperature in the duct?

Treat the air as a perfect gas having $\gamma = 1·4$ and make use of tabulated functions for the Rayleigh line. (Ref 3)

Unworked Problems

8.11 A wall of thermal insulation has a rectangular section 2 m × 0·5 m and is made from timber 150 mm thick, cork board 300 mm thick and steel plate 50 mm thick. The outer timber face is at 28°C and the outer steel face at 150°C. Calculate the temperature differences across each material and the heat flow rate per square metre.

What would be the heat flux if aluminium rods 40 mm diameter were inserted one through each square metre? Assume that the temperatures of the rods at sections flush with the outer faces of the wall are those of the wall surfaces.

The thermal conductivities are: timber 0·11 W/m K, cork 0·035 W/m K, steel 45·0 W/m K, aluminium 204·0 W/m K.

(0·0135 K, 105·23 K, 16·75 K, 12·3 W, 75 W.)

8.12 An experimental test chamber, inside dimensions 20 m × 10 m × 3 m high, is to be maintained at 300°C. The walls and roof consist of brick 120 mm thick insulated with glass wool 80 mm thick protected on the outside by timber 40 mm thick. The surrounding atmospheric temperature is 20°C. Determine the power necessary to keep the chamber at constant temperature using the following data:

Thermal conductivity: brick, 1·4 W/m K
glass wool, 0·043 W/m K
timber, 0·11 W/m K

Heat transfer coefficients for the outer vertical timber surfaces: 1·62 W/m² K
and for the horizontal roof surface: 3·35 W/m² K.

Neglect the heat transfer through the floor and the corners and derive any relations required from the Fourier rate equation.

Calculate also the temperatures at these points:
(a) the interfaces and outer surface of the walls,
(b) the outer surface of the roof.

(38·7 kW, 291·8°C, 113·8°C, 79·0°C, 52°C)

.13 A pipe having an external diameter of 80 mm has lagging 40 mm thick of conductivity 0·18 kJ m/m² h K. Saturated steam at 40 bar flows through this pipe and some condenses, the ambient temperature being 19·5°C. The surface of the lagging has a heat transfer coefficient of 30 kJ/m² h K. What thickness of lagging having a conductivity of 0·25 kJ m/m² h K must be added to reduce the condensation rate by 50 per cent if the surface coefficient is unchanged? The resistance of the pipe and other internal resistances are negligible. (170 mm)

.14 Derive an expression for the resistance of a cylindrical wall to radial heat flow.

A pipe 60 mm in diameter, 100 m long, carries liquid sodium which enters at 1000°C and flows at the rate of 5 kg/s. The pipe is lagged to a radius of 80 mm with a material having a thermal conductivity of 0·043 W/m K which is covered with a further layer 20 mm thick and conductivity 0·1 W/m K, having a surface transfer coefficient of 4·3 W/m² K. The surrounding temperature is 20°C. Determine the temperature of the sodium leaving the pipe. Neglect resistance of the pipe wall and all other internal resistances and ignore the effect of the change of liquid temperature on the mean temperature difference for heat transfer. (996·43°C)

.15 A pipe, having an external diameter of 50 mm, carries saturated ammonia at −30°C and is lagged with foamed plastic to a diameter of 80 mm. The surrounding atmosphere is at 20°C. Calculate from first principles the evaporation rate per metre of pipe length. Conductivity of insulation 0·04 W/m K, surface coefficient 1·1 W/m² K. Neglect the resistance of the pipe and all other internal resistances. (24 g/h)

.16 A spherical pressure vessel, 4·5 m inside diameter, is made from 80 mm thick steel plate and holds gas at 430°C. It is lagged with glass fibre 160 mm thick protected externally by concrete 130 mm thick. Calculate the heat loss rate when the surroundings are at 18°C. The coefficients of thermal conductivity are, for concrete 1·73, glass fibre 0·052 and steel 45 W/m K. The heat transfer coefficient for the outer surface of the concrete is 7·9 W/m² K. (9·25 kW)

.17 A storage tank for liquid methane, CH_4, holds 30 m³ of liquid at 1·01 bar, −161·4°C together with some methane vapour. The tank is a vertical aluminium cylinder 3 m outside diameter, 3·6 m high with

145

a hemispherical top. It is lagged with glass fibre 1 m thick, sheathe with balsa-wood panels 0·2 m thick protected externally by a thin ste case.

Calculate the percentage of the liquid evaporating in 24 hours if th temperature of the steel is 13°C. The thermal resistance of the steel an aluminium shells and the heat transfer through the base are negligibl

The conductivities of balsa-wood and glass fibre are 0·043 an 0·06 W/m K respectively. (0·823 per cen

8.18 The natural convection heat transfer coefficient, h, for square fla plates may be obtained from a relation of the form:

$$Nu = a_1 Gr^{a_2} Pr^{a_3}$$

in which $$Nu = \frac{hL}{k} \text{ and } Gr = \frac{g\beta\Delta T\rho^2 L^3}{\mu^2}$$

where L is the length of side, ΔT is the temperature difference betwee surface and bulk air and g the local weight per unit mass. k, ρ, μ an Pr are the fluid properties listed at the mean film temperature. β is th coefficient of cubical expansion of the fluid at the mean film tempera ture. Calculate the heat transfer by natural convection from a plat 76·2 mm square at 355 K in air at 295 K and 1 atm.

(a) If the plate is in a vertical plane with one edge horizontal.
For this configuration
if $10^4 < Gr\,Pr < 10^9$ take $a_1 = 0·59$, $a_2 = a_3 = 0·25$
if $10^9 < Gr\,Pr < 10^{12}$ take $a_1 = 0·129$, $a_2 = a_3 = 0·33$

(b) If the plate is horizontal.
For top surface:
if $10^5 < Gr\,Pr < 10^8$ take $a_1 = 0·54$, $a_2 = a_3 = 0·25$
if $10^8 < Gr\,Pr$ take $a_1 = 0·14$, $a_2 = a_3 = 0·33$
For bottom surface:
if $10^5 < Gr\,Pr$ take $a_1 = 0·25$, $a_2 = a_3 = 0·25$
Take $g = 9·81$ N/kg $= 9·81$ m/s²

[(a) 5·5 W   (b) 3·7 W

8.19 A duct of circular cross-section 0·7 m diameter, carries CO_2 at 550 F and 1·013 bar. The flow rate is 2500 kg/h and the duct wall is main tained at 316 K. Determine the heat loss per 100 m length of duct Use the correlation $Nu = 0·023\,Re^{0·8}\,Pr^{0·4}$ and take other data from the tables. (323 kW

8.20 A steel pipe, internal diameter 150 mm, carries 100 kg/min of air at 627°C, 4 bar. Lagging limits the heat transfer to the surrounding atmosphere to 500 W/m².

Show, on a sketch of the pipe cross-section, the various thermal resistances involved and indicate their relative importance. Calculate the temperature of the inner steel surface.

For laminar flow of air in a tube:

$$\mathrm{Nu} = 1{\cdot}62\left(\frac{\mu}{\mu_\mathrm{f}}\right)^{\frac{1}{3}}(1 + 0{\cdot}015\ \mathrm{Gr}^{\frac{1}{3}})\left(\frac{4\dot{m}\ c_p}{\pi k L}\right)^{\frac{1}{3}}$$

For turbulent flow of air in a tube:

$$\mathrm{Nu} = 0{\cdot}023\ \mathrm{Re}^{0{\cdot}8}\ \mathrm{Pr}^{0{\cdot}4}$$

(624·85°C)

8.21 Why are liquid metals used as fluids in heat transfer processes? At one point in a tubular exchanger using eutectic liquid 44·5 per cent lead–55·5 per cent bismuth, the temperature is 600 K and the tube wall is at 595 K. The flow rate is 100 kg/min and the tube has an internal diameter of 30 mm. Show that the flow is turbulent and find the heat transfer rate through unit area of tube inner surface. In this case, for turbulent flow, $\mathrm{Nu} = 0{\cdot}625\ (\mathrm{RePr})^{0{\cdot}4}$ where the fluid properties are based on the bulk temperature. (93·45 kW)

8.22 Two parallel square plates each of 4·2 m² area are separated by a gap of 5 mm. One plate has a temperature of 817 K and a surface emissivity of 0·6 while the other has a temperature of 288 K and a surface emissivity of 0·9. Edge effects may be neglected.
(a) Find the rate of heat transfer by radiation between the two plates.
(b) If a thin polished metal sheet of surface emissivity 0·1 both sides is placed centrally in the gap, what will now be the rate of heat transfer by radiation? Assume the two original plate temperatures are unaltered.

Neglect convection effects.   [(a) 59 kW (b) 5·05 kW]

8.23 A horizontal cylinder 76 mm long and 30 mm diameter, well lagged at both ends, is kept at 100°C in a room where the temperature is 15°C.

Calculate the total rates of heat transfer from the cylinder when the surface has an emissivity of (a) 0·3 and (b) 0·9.

147

Take the coefficient of heat transfer by convection as

$$1{\cdot}175\left(\frac{\Delta T}{d}\right)^{0{\cdot}25}\frac{\text{W}}{\text{m}^2\,\text{K}}$$

where ΔT is in kelvins and d in metres.

[(a) 6·75 W (b) 9·77 W]

8.24 A hollow stainless steel electrical conductor has a bore of 10 mm and an outside diameter of 20 mm. Coolant flowing through the tube keeps its internal surface at 100°C and losses keep the external surface at 150°C. The current passing through the conductor is 7000 A. Determine the magnitude and location of the maximum temperature in the conductor.

For stainless steel take $k = 16$ W/m K and the resistivity,

$$\rho = 7{\cdot}0 \times 10^{-7}\,\Omega\,\text{m}.$$

(250°C at 7·61 mm radius)

8.25 A brick wall 0·46 m thick is cooling and measurements indicate that the temperature profile through the wall is given by

$$T = 280 - 300x^2$$

where x is the distance from the hotter face in metres. The brick may be considered as homogeneous having a density 1600 kg/m³, $c_p = 0{\cdot}837$ kJ/kg K and k = 0·7 W/m K.

Calculate the rate of change of temperature at any point in the wall and the energy loss from a section of wall having a face area of 15 m². (1·129 K/h, 2·898 kW)

8.26 Two fluids pass through a heat exchanger, one entering at 150°C and leaving at 82°C, the other entering at 38°C and leaving at 70°C.
(a) What percentage saving in surface area is made by using a counter flow exchanger instead of a parallel flow?
(b) For the parallel flow case find the temperatures of the two fluids at one quarter, one half and three quarters of the way along the exchanger.

[(a) 25·4 per cent; (b) 53·4, 117·4; 62·1, 98·7; 67·1, 88·1°C

8.27 Derive the relationship between the 'Effectiveness' and the NTU for a contra-flow heat exchanger.

Liquid metal, 22 per cent sodium, 78 per cent potassium, at 600°C is cooled to 400°C in a contra-flow heat exchanger where the other fluid is air which enters at 40°C and leaves at 500°C. How much air is heated per kg of NaK liquid? Determine the surface area required for this heat transfer when there is a flow of 1 kg/s of NaK. The overall heat transfer coefficient is 0·2 kW/m² K.   (0·378, 4·45 m²)

8.28 Show that for a single heat exchanger tube where the fluids move in parallel flow

$$\dot{Q}_L = \frac{\Delta T_1}{C}(1 - e^{-CU\pi dL})$$

where $\dot{Q}_L$ is the heat transfer rate in a length L measured from inlet, ΔT_1 is the initial temperature difference, C a constant depending on the flow rates and specific heats of the fluids and U the overall coefficient of heat transfer based on the diameter d.

The following data refers to a simple two-pass parallel flow gas/water heat exchanger in which cross flow regions and conduction through the tube walls are negligible. The tubes have an effective length of 3 m, an outside diameter of 20 mm and there are 25 tubes per pass.

Data:

Water:	flow rate	5 kg/s
	inlet temperature	15°C
	coefficient of heat transfer	4 kW/m² K
Gas:	total flow rate	10 kg/s
	inlet temperature	260°C
	viscosity (μ)	$0·165 \times 10^{-4}$ kg/m s
	conductivity (k)	0·026 W/m K
	specific heat (c_p)	1·05 kJ/kg K
	coefficient of heat transfer (h) given by	$Nu = 0·027\,(Re)^{0·8}$

Determine the gas temperature leaving the first pass.   (147°C)

8.29 A project requires a high speed, high temperature flow of gas. Air is available at 1·15 bar, 450°C (static conditions) and it is proposed to heat this in a smooth tube having a diameter of 150 mm to a stagnation temperature of 1000°C and then expand in a nozzle to the atmospheric pressure of 1·01 bar. The flow rate of the air is 2 kg/s.

Determine the exit diameter at the nozzle, treating the air as a perfect gas which expands isentropically in the nozzle.

Show that the maximum value of the static temperature that it would be possible to achieve during the heating occurs when the Mach Number reaches a value of $\sqrt{(1/\gamma)}$. (162 mm)

8.30 A perfect gas having a specific heat ratio, $\gamma = 1\cdot3$, is cooled in a duct of constant cross-sectional area of $0\cdot05$ m². At point (1) the static pressure and temperature are $3\cdot5$ bar, 600°C and the velocity is 509 m/s. Determine the heat transfer rate required to reduce the static temperature to 297°C. What will the static pressure and velocity be at that point?

Take $R = 0\cdot189$ kJ/kg K. (8·13 MW, 1·73 bar, 674 m/s)

Solutions

8.1 Neglecting the corners the area of flow is

$$2(10 + 8)2\cdot5 + (10 \times 8) = 170 \text{ m}^2$$

The thermal resistance of the wall is

$$R = R_1 + R_2 + R_3$$

where $\dot{Q} = \dfrac{\Delta T}{R}$ and $R = \dfrac{x}{kA}$ for a slab of thickness x, conductivity k

and area A.

$$R = \frac{10^{-3}}{170}\left[\frac{50}{0\cdot2} + \frac{80}{0\cdot04} + \frac{250}{1\cdot8}\right]\frac{K}{W} = 0\cdot0141\,\frac{K}{W}$$

$$\dot{Q} = \frac{40 \text{ K}}{0\cdot0141 \text{ K/W}} = 2840 \text{ W} = \underline{2\cdot84 \text{ kW}}$$

8.2 From the Fourier rate equation

$$\dot{Q} = -k2\pi rL\frac{dT}{dr} \text{ for an elemental cylinder radius } r,$$

thickness dr, length L and having a radial temperature difference dT. Hence for a thick cylindrical shell, inner radius r_i and outer radius r_o

$$\dot{Q}\int_{ri}^{ro}\frac{dr}{r} = -k2\pi L\int_{Ti}^{To} dT$$

$$\dot{Q} = \frac{2\pi kL(T_i - T_o)}{\ln\dfrac{r_o}{r_i}}$$

But
$$\dot{Q} = \frac{\Delta T}{R}$$

Hence
$$R = \frac{\ln \dfrac{r_o}{r_i}}{2\pi k L}$$

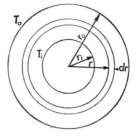

Fig 8.2

For the inner layer
$$R_1 = \frac{\ln \dfrac{175}{75}}{2\pi 0 \cdot 05 \times 100} \frac{K}{m}$$

$$R_2 = \frac{\ln \dfrac{215}{175}}{2\pi 0 \cdot 1 \times 100} \frac{K}{m}$$

The surface resistance is

$$R_3 = \frac{1}{hA} = \frac{1}{8 \times 2\pi \times 215 \times 10^{-3} \times 100} \frac{K}{m}$$

These three resistances are in series between the temperature of saturated steam at 46 bar, *viz* 258·8°C, and the ambient temperature of 18°C

$$\therefore \quad \dot{Q} = \frac{\Delta T}{R_1 + R_2 + R_3}$$

$$= \frac{(258 \cdot 8 - 18)}{\dfrac{1}{2\pi 100}\left[\dfrac{\ln \dfrac{175}{75}}{0 \cdot 05} + \dfrac{\ln \dfrac{215}{175}}{0 \cdot 1} + \dfrac{1000}{8 \times 215}\right]}$$

$$= 7740 \text{ W}$$

h_{fg} at 46 bar = 1668 kJ/kg

$$\text{Condensation rate} = \frac{7 \cdot 74 \text{ kW}}{1668 \text{ kJ/kg}} \times \frac{1 \text{ kJ}}{\text{kWs}} \times 3600 \frac{\text{s}}{\text{h}}$$

$$= \underline{16 \cdot 7 \text{ kg/h}}$$

8.3 Total resistance, R_c, of cylindrical shell and surface

$$= \frac{\ln \dfrac{r_o}{r_i}}{2\pi k L} + \frac{1}{2\pi r_o L h} \qquad \text{(see 8.2)}$$

Now
$$\pi r_i^2 L = 10 \text{ m}^3$$

$$\pi r_i^2 \times 8 r_i = 10 \text{ m}^3$$

$$r_i = \left(\frac{10}{8\pi}\right)^{\frac{1}{3}} = 0 \cdot 737 \text{ m}$$

$$\therefore \quad L = 5 \cdot 9 \text{ m}$$

$$R_c = \frac{\ln \dfrac{0 \cdot 838}{0 \cdot 738}}{2\pi \times 0 \cdot 04 \times 5 \cdot 9} + \frac{1}{2\pi \times 0 \cdot 838 \times 5 \cdot 9 \times 10}$$

$$= 0 \cdot 089 \text{ K/W}$$

Neglecting the corner effects the resistance of the two ends is

$$R_E = \frac{x}{kA} + \frac{1}{hA} = \frac{0 \cdot 1}{0 \cdot 04\pi 0 \cdot 738^2 \times 2} + \frac{1}{10\pi 0 \cdot 738^2 \times 2}$$

$$= 0 \cdot 73 + 0 \cdot 0292 = 0 \cdot 759 \text{ K/W}$$

Total resistance is given by

$$\frac{1}{R} = \frac{1}{R_c} + \frac{1}{R_E} = \frac{1}{0 \cdot 0887} + \frac{1}{0 \cdot 759} = 12 \cdot 598 \text{ W/K}$$

$$\dot{Q} = \frac{\Delta T}{R} = 85 \times 12 \cdot 598 = \underline{1070 \text{ W}}$$

For a spherical vessel to hold 10 m^3

$$r_i = \left(10 \times \frac{3}{4\pi}\right)^{\frac{1}{3}} = \underline{1 \cdot 337 \text{ m}}$$

$$\text{Thermal resistance} = \frac{(r_o - r_i)}{4\pi k r_o r_i} + \frac{1}{h4\pi r_o^2}$$

which must be the same as the resistance of the cylinder if $\dot{Q}$ is to be the same.

$$\frac{4\pi}{12\cdot59} = \frac{(r_o - 1\cdot337)}{0\cdot04 \times 1\cdot337 \times r_o} + \frac{1}{10r_o^2}$$

$$r_o = \underline{1\cdot41 \text{ m}}$$

Hence insulation is 73 mm thick

8.4 (a) Note that the correlation given for h is for laminar flow for a large vertical cylinder in air and is not dimensionless. Other correlations will be found in standard heat transfer references such as Ref 10 Appendix B

$$h = 1\cdot37\left(\frac{184}{1}\right)^{0\cdot25} = 5\cdot04 \text{ W/m}^2 \text{ K}$$

Area of duct surface $= 0\cdot4\pi \times 1 = 1\cdot257 \text{ m}^2$
The heat transfer is then given by the Newton Rate equation

$$\dot{Q} = hA\Delta T$$

$$= 5\cdot04 \frac{\text{W}}{\text{m}^2 \text{ K}} \times 1\cdot257 \text{ m}^2 \times 184 \text{ K} = \underline{1165 \text{ W}}$$

(b) Film temperature $= 102°C = 375 \text{ K}$ at which temperature the tables give $\rho = 0\cdot9413 \text{ kg/m}^3$; $c_p = 1\cdot0106 \text{ kJ/kg K}$;

$$\mu = 2\cdot181 \times 10^{-5} \text{ kg/m s}; k = 3\cdot186 \times 10^{-2} \text{ W/m K}$$

Now $\beta = \frac{1}{v}\left(\frac{\partial v}{\partial T}\right)_p = \frac{1}{T}$ for an ideal gas where $pv = RT$

$$\therefore \quad \beta = \frac{1}{375} = 2\cdot667 \times 10^{-3}$$

Also $g = 9\cdot81 \text{ m/s}^2$

$$\therefore \quad h = \frac{3\cdot186 \times 10^{-2} \times 0\cdot56}{1} \times$$

$$\left[\frac{1^3 \, 2\cdot667 \times 10^{-3} \times 9\cdot81 \times 184 \times 0\cdot9413^2 \times 1010\cdot6}{2\cdot181 \times 10^{-5} \times 3\cdot186 \times 10^{-2}}\right]^{0\cdot25}$$

The units involved here are

$$\frac{W}{m\,K} \times \frac{1}{m}\left[\frac{m^3}{K}\frac{1}{s^2}\frac{m\,K}{}\left(\frac{kg}{m^3}\right)^2 \frac{J}{kg\,K}\frac{m\,s}{kg}\frac{m\,K}{W}\right]^{0\cdot25} = \frac{W}{m^2\,K}$$

Hence

$$h = 5\cdot03\,\frac{W}{\underline{m^2\,K}}$$

8.5 At $52°C = 325$ K, $\mu = 1\cdot962 \times 10^{-5}$ kg/m s

Reynolds number, $\mathrm{Re} = \dfrac{\rho v d}{\mu} = \dfrac{\dot{m}d}{A\mu} = \dfrac{4\dot{m}}{\pi d \mu}$

$$= \frac{4 \times 0\cdot02 \times 10^5}{\pi \times 0\cdot1 \times 1\cdot962} = 13\,000$$

Since this is well in excess of the critical number for flow in tubes (2500) the flow is turbulent and the given correlation applies.

$$\mathrm{Re}^{0\cdot8} = 1950$$

Tables give Prandtl Number, $Pr = 0\cdot701$ at 325 K

$$\therefore \quad Pr^{0\cdot4} = 0\cdot868$$

$$\mathrm{Nu} = 0\cdot023 \times 1950 \times 0\cdot868 = 38\cdot95$$

Now Nusselt Number, $\mathrm{Nu} = \dfrac{hd}{k}$

$$\therefore \quad h = \frac{38\cdot95 \times 2\cdot816 \times 10^{-2}\ \text{W/m K}}{0\cdot1\ \text{m}} = 10\cdot96\ \text{W/m}^2\ \text{K}$$

$$\dot{Q} = hA\Delta T = 10\cdot96 \times \pi 0\cdot1 \times 1 \times 48 = \underline{165\ \text{W}}$$

8.6

This problem may be considered as involving three resistances in series, as shown in fig 8.6, across the potential difference,

$\sigma(T_1^4 - T_2^4)$, where σ is the Stefan-Boltzmann constant.

$$\sigma = 5\cdot67 \times 10^{-8}\ \text{W/m}^2\ \text{K}^4$$

R_1 and R_3 are the 'resistances' associated with the reflectivity of the hot and cold surfaces.

$$R_1 = \frac{1 - \varepsilon_1}{\varepsilon_1 A_1}$$

where ε_1 is the emissivity of the hot surface

Similarly
$$R_3 = \frac{1 - \varepsilon_2}{\varepsilon_2 A_2}$$

R_2 is the resistance associated with the configuration or angle factor, F, between the surfaces.

$$R_2 = \frac{1}{A_1 F_{1-2}} = \frac{1}{A_2 F_{2-1}}$$

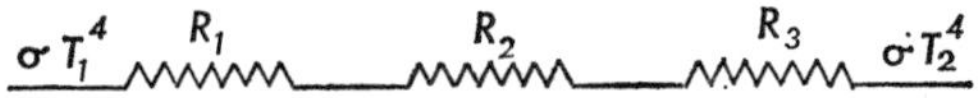

$$\sigma T_1^4 \quad R_1 \qquad\qquad R_2 \qquad\qquad R_3 \quad \sigma T_2^4$$

Fig 8.6

If
$$R = R_1 + R_2 + R_3$$

Then
$$\dot{Q} = \frac{\sigma(T_1^4 - T_2^4)}{R}$$

R is sometimes referred to as the Grey body factor and denoted by $\mathscr{F}$
In the given problem

A_1 = total area of walls and ceiling = $2 \times 6 \cdot 5 + 2 \cdot 625$

$\quad = 15 \cdot 625 \text{ m}^2$

and A_2 = floor area = $2 \cdot 625 \text{ m}^2$

The floor is completely enclosed by the area A_1

$$\therefore \quad F_{2-1} = 1$$

But
$$A_1 F_{1-2} = A_2 F_{2-1}$$

$$\therefore \quad F_{1-2} = \frac{A_2}{A_1} = \frac{2 \cdot 625}{15 \cdot 625} = 0 \cdot 168$$

$$R = \frac{1}{A_1}\left[\frac{1 - 0 \cdot 82}{0 \cdot 82} + \frac{1}{0 \cdot 168} + \frac{1 - 0 \cdot 7}{0 \cdot 7 \times 0 \cdot 168}\right] = 0 \cdot 558 \text{ m}^{-2}$$

$$\dot{Q} = 5 \cdot 67 \times 10^{-8} \frac{\text{W}}{\text{m}^2 \text{ K}^4} \times \frac{10^8 (5 \cdot 23^4 - 4 \cdot 03^4) \text{ K}^4}{0 \cdot 558 \text{ m}^{-2}}$$

$$= 4920 \text{ W} = \underline{4 \cdot 92 \text{ kW}}$$

8.7 Under the conditions specified we can assume that the conduction is one-dimensional and the bar is in steady state. Then the conduction equation reduces to

$$\frac{d^2T}{dx^2} + \frac{\dot{q}}{k} = 0 \qquad (i)$$

where $\dot{q}$ is the rate of heat generation per unit volume.
Integrating twice

$$T + \frac{\dot{q}x^2}{2k} + C_1x + C_2 = 0 \qquad (ii)$$

where C_1 and C_2 are constants.
Now at any section distant x from the insulated face

$$\dot{Q}_x = -kA\left(\frac{dT}{dx}\right)_x \quad \text{by Fourier rate equation.}$$

But at $x = 0$ $\quad \dot{Q}_x = 0 \quad \therefore \quad \left(\frac{dT}{dx}\right)_0 = 0$

Integrating (i) once gives

$$\frac{dT}{dx} + \frac{\dot{q}x}{k} + C_1 = 0$$

$$\frac{\dot{q}x0}{k} + C_1 = 0 \qquad \therefore \quad C_1 = 0$$

At $x = 5 \times 10^{-3}$ m $\quad T = 50°C$

$$\therefore \quad 50 + \frac{\dot{q}(5 \times 10^{-3})^2}{2k} + C_2 = 0$$

$$\dot{q} = \rho i^2 \quad \text{where} \quad i = \left[\frac{6000}{8 \times 5 \times 10^{-5}}\right]\frac{A}{m^2}$$

Note that ρ has units $\Omega\,m = \dfrac{Wm}{A^2}$

$$\therefore \quad \dot{q} = 2 \times 10^{-8}\left[\frac{6000}{8 \times 5 \times 10^{-5}}\right]^2 = 450 \times 10^4 \text{ W/m}^3$$

$$\therefore \quad C_2 = -50 - \frac{450 \times 10^4 \times 25 \times 10^{-6}}{2 \times 380} = -50{\cdot}148$$

Substituting in (ii) $T_0 = \underline{50{\cdot}148°C} = $ Maximum temperature at insulated face.

At the mid point $x = 2 \cdot 5 \times 10^{-3}$ m

$$T_{mid} = \frac{-450 \times 10^4 \times 625 \times 10^{-8}}{2 \times 380} + 50 \cdot 148 = \underline{50 \cdot 111°C.}$$

8.8 In this case of unsteady one dimensional conduction the general conduction equation reduces to

$$\frac{\partial T}{\partial t} = \alpha \left(\frac{\partial^2 T}{\partial x^2} \right) \tag{i}$$

where t is time and α is the thermal diffusivity

$$\alpha = \frac{k}{\rho c_p}$$

Alternatively equation (i) may be deduced by considering the energy balance of an element of the wall section.

Differentiating the given temperature distribution

$$\frac{\partial T}{\partial x} = -360x^2 - 15 \quad \text{and} \quad \frac{\partial^2 T}{\partial x^2} = -720x \frac{K}{m^2}$$

$$\alpha = 0 \cdot 05 \frac{W}{m\,K} \times \frac{1}{237} \frac{m^3}{kg} \times \frac{1}{600} \frac{kg\,K}{J} = 0 \cdot 352 \times 10^{-6} \frac{m^2}{s}$$

$$\therefore \quad \frac{\partial T}{\partial t} = -0 \cdot 352 \times 10^{-6} \times 720x = -253 \cdot 5 \times 10^{-6}\,x$$

When $x = 0$ $\quad \frac{\partial T}{\partial t} = 0$, that is <u>temperature of hot face is constant.</u>

When $x = 1$ m $\quad \frac{\partial T}{\partial t} = -253 \cdot 5 \times 10^{-6} \frac{K}{s} = \underline{-0 \cdot 912 \frac{K}{h}}$

When $x = 0 \cdot 5$ m $\quad \frac{\partial T}{\partial t} = \underline{-0 \cdot 456 \frac{K}{h}}$

Energy stored by an element, width dx will be $c_p \rho A\, dx \left(\frac{\partial T}{\partial t} \right) dt$

Substituting from (i), energy stored $= kA \left(\frac{\partial^2 T}{\partial x^2} \right) dx dt$

Rate of storage in wall $= kA \int \left(\frac{\partial^2 T}{\partial x^2} \right) dx = kA \int_0^1 (-720x) dx$

Rate of storage per m^2 = $0.05 \dfrac{\text{W}}{\text{m K}} \times 1 \text{ m}^2 \left(\dfrac{-720}{2} \right) \dfrac{\text{K}}{\text{m}} = \underline{-18 \text{ W}}$

8.9 For oil $\dot{Q}_0 = \dot{m}_0 c_p \Delta T = 2000 \times 2.51 \times 77 \text{ kJ/h}$

For water $\dot{Q}_w = \dot{m}_w c_p \Delta T = \dot{m}\, 4.18 \times 65$

Energy balance gives $\dot{Q}_0 = \dot{Q}_w$

$$\therefore \quad \dot{m}_w = \frac{2000 \times 2.51 \times 77}{4.18 \times 65} = \underline{1425 \text{ kg/h}}$$

Capacity rate ratio $C = \dfrac{(\dot{m}c_p)_o}{(\dot{m}c_p)_w} = \dfrac{2000 \times 2.51}{1425 \times 4.18} = 0.843$

Effectiveness $E = \dfrac{T_{01} - T_{02}}{T_{01} - T_{w1}} = \dfrac{77}{107 - 15} = \underline{0.837}$

Now for a counter flow exchanger

$$E = \frac{1 - e^{-NTU(1-C)}}{1 - Ce^{-NTU(1-C)}}$$

Rearranging

$$\left[\frac{E-1}{EC-1} \right] = e^{-NTU(1-C)}$$

$$\therefore \quad \frac{0.163}{0.295} = e^{-0.157NTU}$$

$$\ln 0.553 = -0.157 \, NTU$$

$$\frac{0.5924}{0.157} = NTU = 3.77$$

But $\qquad NTU = \dfrac{UA}{(\dot{m}c_p)_o}$

$$\therefore \quad A = \frac{NTU(\dot{m}c_p)_o}{U} = 3.77 \frac{2000 \text{ kg}}{3600 \text{ s}} \times 2510 \frac{\text{kJ}}{\text{kg K}} \times \frac{1}{1.5} \frac{\text{s m}^2 \text{ K}}{\text{kJ}}$$

$$= \underline{3.5 \text{ m}^2}$$

8.10 The acoustic velocity at inlet, $a_1 = (\gamma RT)^{\frac{1}{2}}$
$$= (1.4 \times 0.2871 \times 10^3 \times 393)^{\frac{1}{2}}$$
$$= 397.44 \text{ m/s}$$

$$\text{Ma}_1 = \frac{174.8}{397.4} = 0.44 \text{ since } v_1 = 174.8 \text{ m/s}$$

$$T_{01} = T_1 + \frac{v^2}{2\,c_p} = 393 + \frac{174 \cdot 8^2}{2 \times 1005} = 408 \cdot 2 \text{ K}$$

OR using the *isentropic* table (Ref 3) for Ma $= 0 \cdot 44$

$$T_{01} = \frac{393}{0 \cdot 96272} = 408 \text{ K}$$

From the Rayleigh table with $\gamma = 1 \cdot 4$

$$\text{Ma}_1 = 0 \cdot 44 \qquad \frac{T_{01}}{T_0^*} = 0 \cdot 59748 \qquad \frac{T_1}{T^*} = 0 \cdot 69025 \qquad \frac{p_1}{p^*} = 1 \cdot 8882$$

$$\text{Ma}_2 = 0 \cdot 9 \qquad \frac{T_{02}}{T_0^*} = 0 \cdot 99207 \qquad \frac{T_2}{T^*} = 1 \cdot 02451 \qquad \frac{p_2}{p^*} = 1 \cdot 1246$$

$$\frac{T_{02}}{T_{01}} = \frac{T_{02}}{T^*} \times \frac{T^*}{T_{01}} = \frac{0 \cdot 99207}{0 \cdot 59748} = 1 \cdot 66$$

$$\therefore \quad T_{02} = 1 \cdot 66 \times 408 = 678 \text{ K}$$

$$\therefore \quad \Delta T_0 = 270 \text{ K and } \dot{Q} = \dot{m}\, c_p \Delta T_0$$

$$\dot{m} = \rho v A = \frac{p_1}{RT_1} v_1 A = \frac{400}{0 \cdot 2871 \times 393} \times 174 \cdot 8 \times 0 \cdot 03 = 18 \cdot 6 \text{ kg/s}$$

$$\therefore \quad \dot{Q} = 18 \cdot 6 \times 1 \cdot 005 \times 270 = 5 \cdot 05 \times 10^3 \text{ kW} = \underline{5 \cdot 05 \text{ MW}}$$

$$\frac{T_2}{T_1} = \frac{T_2}{T^*} \times \frac{T^*}{T_1} = \frac{1 \cdot 02451}{0 \cdot 69025} = 1 \cdot 484$$

$$T_2 = 1 \cdot 484 \times 393 = \underline{583 \text{ K}}$$

Similarly
$$p_2 = 4 \times \frac{1 \cdot 1246}{1 \cdot 8882} = \underline{2 \cdot 39 \text{ bar}}$$

The maximum static temperature may be shown (Ref 9 or 12) to occur when

$$\text{Ma} = \left(\frac{1}{\gamma}\right)^{\frac{1}{2}} = \left(\frac{1}{1 \cdot 4}\right)^{\frac{1}{2}} = 0 \cdot 845$$

Here $\frac{T_{\max}}{T^*} = 1 \cdot 02854$ and $T_{\max} = 393 \times \frac{1 \cdot 02854}{0 \cdot 69025} = \underline{585 \text{ K}}$

Appendix A

TABLE 1

Standardised Enthalpies for Gases at Low Pressure (kJ/kg mole)

T, K	O₂	N₂	H₂	Air	H₂O	CO	CO₂	Monatomics
298	0	0	0	0	−241829	−110524	−393519	0
350	1524	1505	1496	1562	−240111	−109018	−391541	959
400	3018	2965	2952	3081	−238409	−107555	−389523	2122
450	4535	4431	4411	4550	−236685	−106083	−387413	3152
500	6077	5904	5873	6045	−234938	−104600	−385221	4191
550	7645	7389	7332	7542	−233164	−103102	−382955	5231
600	9238	8888	8977	8936	−231362	−101588	−380620	6270
650	10854	10402	10343	10467	−229532	−100057	−378223	7309
700	12494	11931	11726	12014	−227672	−98507	−375770	8348
750	14154	13478	13213	13580	−225781	−96939	−373146	9388
800	15832	15042	14691	15163	−223860	−95352	−370484	10427
850	17528	16623	16175	16763	−221908	−93748	−367874	11466
900	19239	18220	17665	18379	−219924	−92127	−365182	12506
950	20964	19833	19163	20012	−217908	−90489	−362547	13545
1000	22703	21461	20669	21655	−215860	−88837	−359113	14584
1050	24453	23104	22185	23275	−213780	−87170	−357275	15624
1100	26214	24762	23710	24925	−211668	−85491	−354619	16663
1150	27984	26432	25244	26637	−209524	−83798	−351833	17702
1200	29764	28114	26789	28363	−207351	−82094	−349024	18742
1250	31552	29808	28344	30077	−205147	−80379	−346192	19781
1300	33348	31512	29910	31793	−202914	−78654	−343341	20820
1350	35152	33225	31486	33518	−200652	−76921	−340471	21860
1400	36963	34947	33073	35252	−198364	−75178	−337583	22899
1450	38782	36679	34671	36996	−196048	−73428	−334679	23938
1500	40606	38418	36279	38746	−193707	−71669	−331760	24977

For liquid H₂O at 298 k h = − 285 782

160

T, K	O₂	N₂	H₂	Air	H₂O	CO	CO₂	Monatomics
1550	42438	40165	37899	40503	−191341	−69905	−328827	26017
1600	44275	41919	39529	42268	−188951	−68133	−325880	27056
1650	46119	43680	41171	44039	−186539	−66356	−322921	28095
1700	47969	45447	42822	45817	−184106	−64574	−319950	29135
1750	49825	47220	44484	47600	−181651	−62786	−316968	30174
1800	51687	48998	46156	49388	−179176	−60993	−313976	31213
1850	53554	50782	47837	51182	−176682	−59195	−310975	32253
1900	55428	52570	49528	52981	−174169	−57393	−307964	33292
1950	57308	54363	51227	54785	−171639	−55587	−304945	34332
2000	59193	56161	52935	56593	−169091	−53776	−301918	35371
2050	61085	57962	54651	58406	−166527	−51962	−298884	36410
2100	62982	59768	56375	60224	−163947	−50144	−295842	37449
2150	64884	61577	58107	62045	−161352	−48322	−292794	38489
2200	66792	63390	59847	63871	−158604	−46497	−289739	39528
2250	68706	65207	61594	65700	−156065	−44669	−286678	40567
2300	70625	67026	63348	67533	−153415	−42838	−283611	41606
2350	72549	68849	65109	69370	−150785	−41005	−280538	42646
2400	74479	70675	66878	71209	−148146	−39169	−277459	43685
2450	76414	72503	68653	73052	−145501	−37330	−274374	44724
2500	78355	74335	70434	74898	−142817	−35489	−271284	45764
2550	80301	76168	72220	76748	−140122	−33646	−268189	46803
2600	82251	78004	74074	78655	−137416	−31800	−265089	47842
2650	84207	79843	75839	80500	−134700	−29953	−261984	48882
2700	86168	81683	77616	82345	−131975	−28103	−258874	49921
2750	88133	83526	79453	84247	−129241	−26252	−255760	50960

TABLE 2

Absolute Entropies for Gases at 1 atm (kJ/kg mole K)

T, K	O₂	N₂	H₂	Air	H₂O	CO	CO₂	Monatomics
298	205·095	191·567	130·603	194·000	188·737	197·918	213·661	154·669
350	209·791	196·598	135·226	198·649	194·113	202·572	219·777	158·069
400	213·777	200·225	139·115	202·559	198·660	206·482	225·164	160·848
450	217·344	203·425	142·551	206·026	202·720	209·949	230·134	163·296
500	220·594	206·627	145·634	209·152	206·401	213·075	234·754	165·483
550	223·580	209·513	148·422	212·010	209·781	215·929	239·072	167·464
600	226·352	212·065	150·974	214·643	212·915	218·565	243·139	169·276
650	228·941	214·486	153·323	217·092	215·843	221·018	246·975	170·941
700	231·369	216·753	155·500	219·388	218·604	223·315	250·609	172·480
750	233·657	218·887	157·533	221·548	221·213	225·477	254·065	173·913
800	235·824	220·906	159·444	223·590	223·692	227·523	257·359	175·254
850	237·881	222·825	161·243	225·530	226·062	229·468	260·506	176·513
900	239·835	224·648	162·945	227·328	228·332	231·324	263·518	177·703
950	241·698	226·394	164·567	229·289	230·508	233·096	266·407	178·827
1000	243·483	228·063	166·111	231·053	232·614	234·787	269·178	179·894
1050	245·191	229·665	167·592	232·597	234·645	236·415	271·847	180·907
1100	246·829	231·207	169·011	233·953	236·615	237·981	274·415	181·875
1150	248·400	232·696	170·374	235·501	238·523	239·486	276·891	182·798
1200	249·915	234·127	171·688	236·946	240·374	240·934	279·282	183·683
1250	251·375	235·508	172·959	238·339	242·176	242·335	281·595	184·530
1300	252·783	236·846	174·187	239·684	243·931	243·690	283·833	185·345
1350	254·143	238·140	175·377	240·987	245·639	245·000	286·000	186·130
1400	255·458	239·442	176·535	242·249	247·305	246·269	288·102	186·884
1450	256·736	240·603	177·656	243·471	248·934	247·495	290·138	187·615
1500	257·974	241·772	178·743	244·660	250·526	248·688	292·117	188·322

For liquid H₂O at 298 k S = 40·910

162

T, K	O_2	N_2	H_2	Air	H_2O	CO	CO_2	Monatomics
1550	259·174	242·915	179·803	245·815	252·076	249·846	294·046	189·002
1600	260·340	244·098	180·839	246·932	253·536	250·971	295·917	189·661
1650	261·472	245·127	181·852	248·021	255·120	252·064	297·735	190·303
1700	262·578	246·183	182·839	249·083	256·535	253·127	299·510	190·916
1750	263·656	247·211	183·802	250·117	257·964	254·164	301·241	191·508
1800	264·702	248·215	184·745	251·124	259·365	255·175	302·927	192·085
1850	265·724	249·196	185·666	252·107	260·735	256·160	304·573	192·665
1900	266·727	250·148	186·565	253·068	262·079	257·122	306·178	193·215
1950	267·703	251·076	187·448	254·003	263·395	258·060	307·743	193·767
2000	268·659	251·987	188·314	254·922	264·694	258·975	309·279	194·301
2050	269·590	252·877	189·163	255·816	265·961	259·872	310·777	194·807
2100	270·505	253·747	189·994	256·693	267·208	260·750	312·244	195·312
2150	271·400	254·599	190·809	257·550	268·431	261·607	313·677	195·797
2200	272·274	255·436	191·609	258·389	269·636	262·446	315·084	196·278
2250	273·135	256·249	192·397	259·212	270·820	263·269	316·462	196·746
2300	273·980	257·046	193·166	260·017	271·810	264·072	317·810	197·201
2350	274·807	257·833	193·920	260·807	273·124	264·859	319·132	197·651
2400	275·620	258·604	194·667	261·582	274·249	265·635	320·426	198·087
2450	276·417	259·359	195·399	262·341	275·354	266·394	321·699	198·518
2500	277·200	260·097	196·118	263·086	276·446	267·139	322·949	198·936
2550	277·973	260·825	196·827	263·818	277·517	267·867	324·175	199·351
2600	278·729	261·536	197·526	264·543	278·571	268·584	325·380	199·752
2650	279·471	262·235	198·212	265·246	279·611	269·289	326·562	200·149
2700	280·205	262·923	198·886	265·938	280·633	269·980	327·726	200·537
2750	280·930	263·599	199·551	266·623	281·637	270·659	328·870	200·917

Converted by computer programme from Table B 13 of *Thermodynamics*, W. C. Reynolds (McGraw-Hill, 1965). Rounding off to 4 or 5 significant figures will normally suffice.

Appendix B

BIBLIOGRAPHY AND REFERENCES

1. Haywood, R. W., *Thermodynamic Tables in SI Units* (Cambridge University Press, 1968)
2. Hickson, D. C. and Taylor, F. R., *Enthalpy-Entropy Diagram for Steam* (*mks*) (Blackwell)
3. Keenan, J. H. and Kaye, J., *Gas Tables* (Wiley, 1948)
4. Mayhew, Y. R. and Rogers, G. F. C., *Thermodynamic and Transport Properties of Fluids in SI Units* (Blackwell, 1967)
5. *N.E.L. Steam Tables 1964* (H.M. Stationery Office)
6. Reynolds, W. C., *Thermodynamics* (McGraw-Hill, 1968)
7. Rogers, G. F. C. and Mayhew, Y. R., *Engineering Thermodynamics, Work and Heat Transfer. SI Units* (Longmans, 1967)
8. Schenck, H., *Heat Transfer Engineering* (Longmans, 1960)
9. Shapiro, A. H., *The Dynamics and Thermodynamics of Compressible Fluid Flow* (Ronald Press, 1953)
10. Simonson, J. R., *An Introduction to Engineering Heat Transfer* (McGraw-Hill, 1967)
11. Smith, H. J. and Harris, J. W., *Basic Thermodynamics for Engineers* (MacDonald, 1966)
12. Wallace, F. J. and Linning, W. A., *Basic Engineering Thermodynamics* (Pitman, 1968)
13. Van Wylen, G. J., and Sonntag, R. E., *Fundamentals of Classical Thermodynamics* (Wiley, 1965)